ANTARCTIC WORLD

JOHN EULLE

ANTARCTIC

Illustrated with Photographs, Maps and Diagram

 **WORLD**

ABELARD-SCHUMAN
London New York Toronto

LONDON	NEW YORK	TORONTO
Abelard-Schuman	*Abelard-Schuman*	*Abelard-Schuman*
Limited	*Limited*	*Canada Limited*
38 Russell Square	*6 West 57th Street*	*81 John Street*

Printed in the United States of America

CONTENTS

1. Preliminaries 11

2. The Face of Antarctica 16

3. The Face of Antarctica (cont'd) 26

4. Sealers and Sailors 34

5. Magnetism, Fire, and Ice 48

6. To the Uttermost Point 59

7. Trial and Tribulation 72

8. Whale Oil and Maps 84

9. Men Among the Penguins 101

10. Flying the Antarctic 115

11. Operation Deepfreeze:
     Plan and Preparation 130

12. IGY: The Combined Assault 143

13. Midcentury Traverses 164

14. *Homo Sapiens Antarcticus* 182

15. Who Owns Antarctica and Why
     Do They Want It? 200

16. Antarctica and You 214

ILLUSTRATIONS

MAPS AND CHARTS

Ice features	19
The face of Antarctica	24
Comparison of antarctic climates	27
The presumed circulation over Antarctica	29
The discovery of Antarctica, 1820	41
The Ross Ice Shelf	55
Journeys to the Uttermost Point, 1911-12, ending in triumph and tragedy	70
Shackleton's escape from the ice, one of the most daring small-boat voyages in modern history	81
A comparison of various whales encountered in the antarctic; graphic illustration showing size of blue whale	89
Euphausia superba, the shrimp-like organism which is principal food of baleen whales	91
The aerial explorations of Richard E. Byrd	128
Some of the important IGY antarctic stations	145
Plan of United States IGY Amundsen-Scott Station at the south pole, 1958	150
A profile along a traverse into Marie Byrd Land; a profile at the south pole	156
The real Antarctica? A hypothetical map based on recent seismic explorations	158
Midcentury traverses in quest of knowledge for IGY	177
Antarctic pie. Several nations claim territory	203

PHOTOGRAPHS

Captain James Cook   10

Possession Bay in the island of South Georgia   14

A flat-topped tabular berg   22

An antarctic snowscape   32

Captain Nathaniel Brown Palmer   38

A herd of elephant seals on beach in South Georgia   46

Mount Erebus, antarctic volcano first seen by Ross, a
    link in the "ring of fire"   53

Beardmore Glacier, largest valley glacier in the world   62

Scott's party at the pole, cold and haggard, facing cruel
    journey home   68

The launching of the *James Caird,* elephant Island,
    1916   78

A modern whale catcher   94

The ribs are torn loose from a blue whale   97

Blubber is cut off in strips and then sent to cookers
    below   99

Emperor penguins   106

Royal penguins crowd the beach on Macquarie Island   112

The *Floyd Bennett* at Little America   119

Citroën tractor, first successful oversnow motor vehicle,
    used by Byrd on his second antarctic expedition   122

Vessel unloading at Kainan Bay during Operation
    Deepfreeze   133

U.S.S. Glacier breaking her way through light sea ice
    in McMurdo Sound   135

Que Sera Sera, first airplane to land at the south pole   140

United States Ellsworth Station under construction   148

Sir Vivian Fuch's Sno-cats on the trail   168

Australian DUKW vehicles churn through the ice and
    then crawl up onto the shore   175

United States Navy tractor train on the road to Byrd
    Station   179

Homo Sapiens Antarcticus dressed for an outing   187

Surveyors engaged in mapmaking near Mawson Station   189

An American party raises the American flag in Marie
    Byrd Land, 1939   206

American Servicemen at a dedication ceremony at Mc-
    Murdo Sound   208

Rear Admiral George Dufek, commander of Operation
    Deepfreeze, 1956   212

Captain James Cook, the English navigator who failed to discover Antarctica but crossed the antarctic circle three times and established the limits within which the continent must lie.

1

Preliminaries

JAMES COOK so distinguished himself on an astronomical expedition to Tahiti, he was promoted from lieutenant to commander and instantly seized upon to lead a second expedition into the southern hemisphere, an enterprise which the British Admiralty calculated would settle the antarctic problem once and for all.

Regarding the man, the Admiralty could not have judged more wisely, for Cook has since been acclaimed one of the illustrious naval personages of the 18th Century. Regarding the antarctic problem, the Admiralty was in water over its head. In 1772, when Cook sailed on his ambitious voyage, the very existence of an antarctic continent was absolutely unknown. Not a single extant fact was at hand concerning the nature of the globe south of the antarctic circle, which line had indeed yet to be crossed. But there were fancies galore. Cook was to explore as much of the continent as possible and make "observations of every kind as might be useful." He was to invite the inhabitants to trade with England, and he was to show them "every kind of civility and regard."

The idea of a southern continent was not new. Two thousand years before, Greek philosophers, already acquainted with the fact that the earth is a sphere, reasoned that there should be a southern land mass to give the globe

symmetry, and to balance the weight of the known northern lands. Greek theories about astronomy and climate
indicated that this continent should be cold and capped
with eternal ice, but unapproachable because of the barrier
presented by the flaming tropics. For a civilization that
had not yet traveled far from the Mediterranean, it was a
remarkable guess.

Subsequently much of what the Greeks surmised was
forgotten or disproved, but the idea of a southern continent stuck in men's minds. The geographers of the 16th
and 17th Centuries were disappointed by the voyages of
discovery that showed Africa and South America were not
northern extensions of the unknown southern land—*Terra
Australis Nondum Incognita,* as it was called. In 1575 the
Dutchman A. Ortelius, a renowned and imaginative map-
maker, represented it as a great sprawling continent that
covered fully one-third of the globe.

For two centuries the navigators of Spain, France, Hol-
land, Portugal, and England pressed southward, finding
water in the places where Ortelius had drawn land. By
Cook's time the fanciful Dutchman had been thoroughly
discredited—but the idea still lingered that somewhere
beyond the limits of exploration a vast continent lay waiting for discovery. Cook's principal object was to find this
continent or, on the other hand, disprove its existence.

For the voyage Cook chose the *Resolution* and *Adventure,* vessels sturdily built for the coal trade and therefore
able to withstand the rigors of storm and ice. The ships
were provisioned for two years. In addition to the usual
crews, they carried a scientific staff consisting of a natural-
ist, two astronomers, and an artist "to depict the places
and people met with." Cook took his departure from Cape
Town in November, 1772.

During the next three seasons he completed voyages

which, when pieced together, circled the earth in latitudes generally south of 60 degrees. In both hemispheres he sailed far south of the tracks of all previous ships. He ploughed through dismal seas strewn with ice and swept by storm. "We were almost perpetually wrapped in thick fogs, beaten with showers of rain, sleet, hail, and snow, surrounded by innumerable islands of ice (icebergs), against which we daily ran the risk of being shipwrecked, and forced to live on salt provisions, which concurred with the cold and wet to infect the mass of our blood." He sailed and sailed across areas where romancers had envisioned land. He sliced off great chunks of the unknown. But no continent was discovered.

In January, 1773, the *Resolution* crossed the antarctic circle, the first vessel ever to do so. Progress to the south was stopped by ice, and no land was to be seen. Twice more Cook crossed the circle, pierced the "frigid zone" of the ancients, found only water with ice blocking the way farther south. Hope turned to skepticism, for if a continent did exist beyond the ice, it was a country ". . . condemned to everlasting rigidity by Nature, never to yield to the warmth of the sun, for whose wild and desolate aspect I find no words . . ."

One discovery eased his disappointment, although it convinced him of the hostility of the antarctic regions. The island of South Georgia, glimpsed through mists a century before by de la Roche, was seen again and briefly explored. Landings were made at various points, a flag was raised, and the isle was claimed for England "under a discharge of small arms."

This was the first discovery of an antarctic land, although its latitude is such that today it is called subantarctic. Cook observed the masses of ice descending into the heads of bays, breaking off, and floating out to sea. If the coast was repellent, "the inner parts of the country were not less savage and horrible. The wild rocks raised their lofty summits till they were lost in the clouds, and the valleys lay covered with everlasting snow. Not a tree was to be seen, not a shrub even big enough to make a tooth-pick." But the shores swarmed with seals and penguins and sea birds, and all these Cook carefully noted. South Georgia was only a small island, not the continent he sought. "I must confess the disappointment I now met with did not affect me much; for to judge of the bulk by the sample it would not be worth the discovery." Satisfied that he had done what he could, Cook sailed for home.

Despite its negative results, the voyage was pronounced a great one. Cook had surpassed all others in the push to the south. His records were meticulous, his chart of South Georgia unsurpassed for a century. The track of his ship in

Possession Bay in the island of South Georgia, Cook's only discovery of land in the antarctic regions. The artist's exaggeration contributes to a forbidding scene.

New York Public Library

what is now the Ross Sea was not crossed until 1934. His achievement was all the more remarkable for he had been born of humble farm folk and ran away to sea from an unpromising apprenticeship in a grocer's shop. His formal education was scant; in the demanding arts of seamanship, pilotage, navigation, astronomy, and leadership he was entirely self-taught. In a day when wealth counted more toward advancement than wisdom, the feat of getting ahead on one's own was almost impossible.

Cook had not solved the antarctic problem. But he had set its limits and, in effect, cleaned the slate for those who would follow. There was to be no "great" continent; it must be contained within Cook's track. It promised no inhabitants, no vegetation, only cold and ice and hostility to man. Cook saw the antarctic as valueless; for one hundred and fifty years he was very nearly right.

But beyond Cook's track *did* lie a continent, a sprawling mass six million square miles in extent, shaped like a looking glass, thickly blurred by ice. Ideas and knowledge spring eternally, and in that one hundred and fifty years the antarctic has grown to occupy an important place in man's thinking. This book is about that remote world, its face which Cook never saw, its fortunes of which he could not dream, its problems which are not yet all solved.

2

The Face of Antarctica

HELEN OF TROY was a mythical Greek woman who had a face that launched a thousand ships. It is presumed her beauty did the trick, a cold and chilling kind of beauty that, doubtless, moved men as well as ships. If true, she has a colossal counterpart in Antarctica.

The late Admiral Richard E. Byrd was fond of ascribing feminine qualities to Antarctica. A pale sleeping princess, he called her, sinister and beautiful in her frozen slumber . . . weirdly luminous with her amethysts and emeralds of ice . . . sirenlike . . . painted in shades of pink, gold, green, and blue. This face has launched not a thousand ships but a billion icebergs.

Ice is Antarctica's most abundant possession, and it must form a major feature of any portrait of her. Unfortunately it has until lately been a mask, hiding most of the details we should like to see. Thus while most continental portraits are first concerned with mountains, plateaus, and plains, in the case of Antarctica it is better to begin with the ice.

Most of us assume a familiarity with ice that is not warranted by experience. We know it as a hard glassy substance which comes from the refrigerator and is useful in making lemonade. Or it is something to skate on in winter. But this ice has been frozen from water and is quite unlike most of the ice in the world—including the 6,000,000-square-mile ice cap on Antarctica—which has been made from snowflakes.

The feat of transforming snow into ice is not as unlikely

as it seems, for snowflakes are in reality delicate crystals of ice. After falling on a surface, agents such as the wind, the warmth of the sun, and the weight of overlying layers begin a compacting process which drives the crystals closer together, deforming them and reducing the amount of air space between them. Soon an intermediate substance called *firn* is formed. Firn is described as something no longer snow but not yet ice. It is a dense material in which the particles are to some extent joined together but in which the air spaces still communicate with each other.

As successive layers of snow accumulate on the firn, the pressure of their weight completes the compacting process, the air spaces virtually disappear, and a solid mass of glacier ice is developed. Because of the method of its formation, this ice has a granular structure and contains a certain amount of entrapped air. A piece of it brought up from deep in a glacier and put into water will effervesce mildly as the air escapes.

The condition necessary for the formation of such ice is that the summer temperature be cool enough so the winter snow does not entirely melt. This condition is met in several high mountain regions of the world, such as the Alps and Andes, in Greenland—which has accumulated the largest continental glacier in the northern hemisphere —and pre-eminently in Antarctica, where the accumulation has been going on for many millions of years and has succeeded in impounding 4½ million *cubic miles* of ice. This is a small but notable fraction of the earth's total water supply.

Because of the layer-upon-layer process of formation, it might be expected that the antarctic ice cap would have grown upward through the centuries and by now resemble an immense white top hat. The reason this has not happened is that glacier ice has a remarkable property. It is not a rigid solid such as iron and granite are imagined to be, but a quasi-liquid—a substance which apparently has some of the properties of a liquid while remaining a solid!

A liquid flows because its individual particles, molecules, are loosely bound together and therefore may freely slide over each other. We may imagine the same phenomenon to occur in a mass of glacier ice, except that the particles are not molecules but much larger "grains" of ice, and there is much more resistance to the movement of the grains because they are frozen together. The "flow" of glacier ice is therefore very slow, three million times slower than the flow of water in, say, the Mississippi River. The precise mechanics of ice movement is complex, but the results are readily apparent. A mass of glacier ice spreads out in whatever direction it may, like a lump of cold molasses on a dinner plate. In Antarctica the inexorable creeping process has long since completely covered the continent with a lofty white dome rising in places to an altitude in excess of 14,000 feet above sea level.

Indeed, if we consider only the ice, Antarctica is by far the loftiest of all continents. But beneath the ice lies evidence of a different story. Echo-sounding techniques have enabled us to determine the thickness of the ice and hence the altitude of the rock base on which it rests. The unexpected part is that the ice cap is of very great thickness, so thick, in fact, that regardless of the altitude of the ice surface the underlying rock is quite low and in places actually below sea level. Our concept of a "lofty" continent will doubtless be much altered as more information is available. (See Chapter 12.)

The antarctic ice cap is not a featureless dome; it has its ups and downs and undulations. But glacier ice being what it is, its topography is somewhat smoother than an ordinary countryside. In the region called East Antarc-

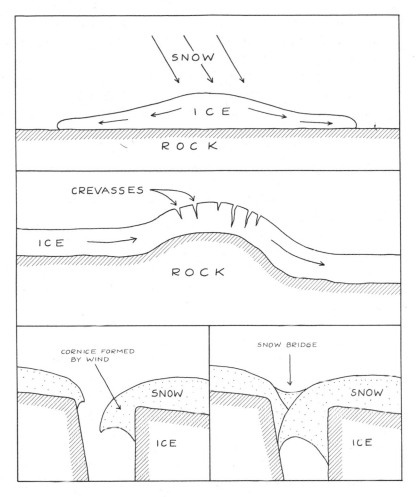

Ice features. Top: movement of ice in a continental glacier; thickness exaggerated, smoothness of bedrock idealized. Center: formation of crevasses as ice passes over obstruction. Bottom: bridging of a crevasse by the growth of snow cornices.

tica, which lies roughly in the eastern hemisphere, is a conspicuous rise with its summit near the Pole of Relative Inaccessibility. This tantalizing point is most remote from all shores and is theoretically the most difficult to reach.

In smaller West Antarctica, which includes the Palmer-Graham peninsula, is another, smaller, ice rise. Between the two is an elongated depression which runs roughly from the Ross Sea to the Weddell Sea. This trench—called the Ross-Weddell Graben on some maps—has been the subject of debate and speculation for many years. It is widely accepted as an indication that East and West Antarctica are separate land masses and would be separated by a wide strait if there were no ice cap. But the hypothesis of a divided continent has not been proved, and until more information about the subglacial surface is obtained, it remains one of the unresolved problems of the antarctic.

The smooth face of the ice cap is here and there disrupted by mountains which thrust up above the surface. The Palmer-Graham peninsula is a long chain of peaks which rise above the surrounding sea and ice like the armored spine of a prehistoric monster. These mountains are an extension of the Andes, which may be traced in an arc across the ocean gap between South America and Antarctica. South Georgia and the islands of the South Orkneys are the tips of Andean peaks which spring from the ocean floor. Following it south, the whole grand system is lost to view as it dips below the surface of the inland ice.

In East Antarctica is another great system of mountains which stand on the western edge of the Ross Sea and run in the direction of the pole. These mountains have been formed by a vertical upthrust of gigantic blocks of sedimentary rocks, a formation which the geologist calls a *horst.* Of late the name Antarctic Horst has been applied to the entire chain, although it is comprised of many individually named ranges and peaks. Where the sediments are accessible the paleontologist may read evidence of an unexplained past: a tropical climate, coal-forming forests, and primitive animal life. We must conclude that Antarctica was once a far different place from what it is today.

The ice creeps in its sluggish swirls through and around everything. It appears as if a battle were in progress, and where the mountains have the upper hand the ice is forced to flow between them in long streams—the largest valley glaciers in the world. Elsewhere the ice has cut a member from the band to form a *nunatak,* an isolated peak all but drowned by the ice, only its summit above the mass. The mountains bear the marks of combat; many have had their slopes eroded by the ice to a sharp pyramidal form suggestive of the Matterhorn. The ice is not unscathed either, for where it meets stress in passing around or over obstructions the surface splits to form *crevasses*—the deep fissures in the ice which are to the traveler a dangerous feature of the antarctic scene. But ultimately the ice prevails and its inexorable spreading out is halted only at the sea, and here the implacable pale face of Antarctica crumbles and disintegrates like the edge of a round tea biscuit in the hands of a hungry little boy.

If the ice had its way, it would cover the sea as it has covered the land. Indeed, in sheltered places it has done so, and formed *ice shelves*—giant floating rafts of ice hundreds of feet thick, hundreds of square miles in extent, and semiattached to the main ice cap on the landward edge. But here at the sea are forces with which the ice at last cannot reckon: the tide, which is irresistible in its power to lift and break; ocean currents which silently carry the broken pieces away. The seaward edge of the ice cap is the birthplace of antarctic icebergs, and here is done all the mighty launching that a hundred Helens could never do.

Icebergs broken from shelf ice are called tabular bergs; they are beautifully flat-topped, like a table; they are characteristic of the antarctic; they make a specialty of bigness. Many could serve as super-aircraft carriers; many more have undoubtedly exceeded in size Manhattan Island, which is two and a half miles wide by thirteen miles long. In the short time that man has observed such matters, some icebergs have been as big as the state of Rhode Island (which to be sure is the smallest state, but very

A flat-topped tabular berg. This specimen, almost 100 feet high, floats quietly in McMurdo Sound.

Official U.S. Navy Photo

large for an iceberg) and also as big as Connecticut—
which is bigger both as a state and as an iceberg.

Speaking of time, how old is the ice in an iceberg?
Obviously icebergs are not made in a hurry. The eminent
German glaciologist Dr. F. Loewe has made a calculation
based on ice movement from the interior of the ice cap
toward the coast, and has arrived at the "probably exaggerated" speed of one hundred fifty feet per year. At this
rate it will take ice formed in the middle of the ice cap
20,000 years to reach the sea. Putting it another way,
icebergs now breaking off fell as snow one hundred fifty
centuries before the Egyptians began recording mankind's
history.

Once loosed, the icebergs march northward in a white
phalanx to warmer waters, where ultimately even the
biggest are destroyed by melting. Just as ice cubes chill
our lemonade, so the annual admixture of billions of tons
of glacial ice chills the adjacent sea. Antarctica is surrounded by a band of cold water, low in salt content and
unexpectedly (to the layman) rich in life. As in the far
north, cold water does not necessarily discourage life; the
multitudinous bizarre forms of the tropics are missing,
but we have in their place more vigorous, more highly
developed, and more useful forms. The sea is the exclusive
habitat of the only truly antarctic fauna: seals, walruses,
whales, penguins, and sea birds. It is also a veritable
"soup" of small microscopic forms which stand at the
bottom of the antarctic food chain, but which may one
day interest man as a source of human food when traditional supplies can no longer support the burgeoning
population.

In winter the surface of the sea freezes, forming salt-
water ice with a maximum thickness of about fifteen feet.
This would be a smooth floating sheet similar to an ice

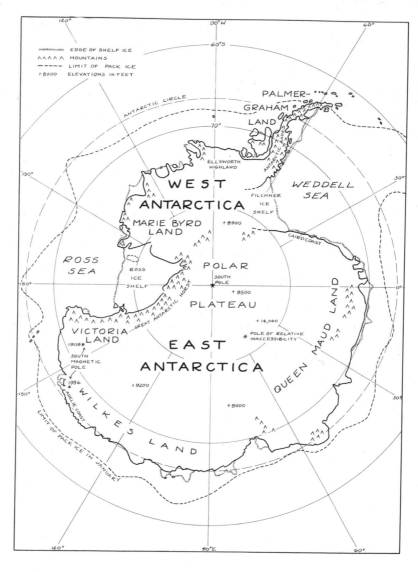

The face of Antarctica; only the mountains protrude above the eternal ice, which rises to 14,000 feet above the sea.

shelf, were it not for the action of wind and currents, which break it into a mosaic of separate floes. In winter the ice hugs the coast; in summer it is freed to drift northward. In a given situation the ice may be "open," with wide channels of water between the floes; under other circumstances it may be powerfully jammed together in overlapping layers of *pressure ice* many times the thickness of the undisturbed floes. This is the ice pack, a low shifting fortress wall that has been Antarctica's best protection against intruders and the nemesis of every captain who has taken a ship into the far south.

North of the pack, along a sharp line of demarcation, the colder, heavier antarctic waters sink beneath the surface and become a part of the greater oceanic circulations. This line, where warm and cold water converge, is called the Antarctic Convergence. It marks sharp changes in sea temperatures, in sea life, and in atmospheric conditions above the surface. To the geographer it is the boundary of the antarctic regions; to our portrait, not yet complete, it is the frame.

3

The Face of Antarctica (cont'd)

A PORTRAIT SHOULD present a hint of personality—the thoughts and moods that lie behind the smile or frown. In the case of Antarctica this can only mean the weather and the climate. Byrd wrote, ". . . her dreams are iridescent ice halos around the sun and moon." Some have denounced her as the "home of the blizzard," and others, seeing another side, call her "the land of silence." One man simply says, "Cold!"

Climate and weather are related, but they are not the same. Weather is the state of the atmosphere at any given time; it is what we see when we open the door in the morning. It comes in a hundred different varieties, and in Antarctica most of them are unpleasant. Climate is the average over an extended period of all the different weathers, and while this tends to lessen some of the extremes, the result in Antarctica is not a happy one.

The data upon which our concept of climate is principally based are temperature and precipitation. If we add to these knowledge of the time of the year when each occurs, a brief yet comprehensive picture is formed of the conditions prevailing. Accompanying are several charts on which these variables for several antarctic locations are shown graphically. The annual march of temperature is shown by the heavy line, which is derived from monthly averages and may be read on the scale at the right. Precipitation is shown by the shaded bars, which show monthly totals and may be read on the scale at the left. Note that in the southern hemisphere the seasons are reversed and

26

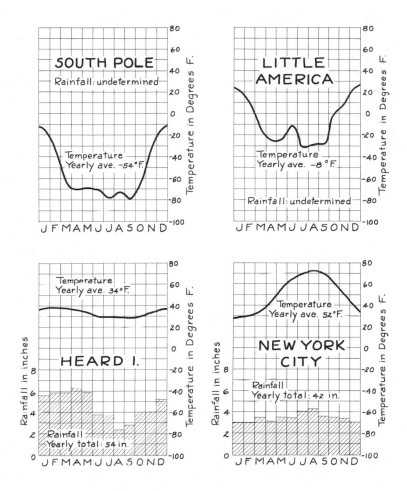

Comparison of antarctic climates. Heard Island has a sub-antarctic maritime climate with little change in temperature during the year. The south pole, with one of the earth's coldest climates, never has a temperature above freezing. Little America is similar but milder. New York City is included for comparison with temperate regions.

the coldest months are July, August and September.

It is apparent that the antarctic regions have several climates. One is associated with the oceanic fringe and is found in islands, such as Heard Island, which lie inside the Antarctic Convergence. Because of the influence of the sea this climate is surprisingly mild; the annual temperature ranges from a few degrees above 32 to a few degrees below. Because of the relative coolness of the air and its limited ability to hold water vapor, the rainfall is not excessive, although it occurs throughout the year. A characteristic not shown by the chart is the storminess of the climate. In these latitudes both wind and water circle the globe in a nearly unbroken sweep; they mercilessly pound any land audacious enough to rise above the surface of the sea. The single word which best describes this often-overlooked antarctic climate is *raw*.

In the interior of the continent quite different conditions prevail; here temperature at least is as we expect it. It is cold, cold, and more cold through the year. In the interior the coldest temperatures known to man have been recorded: in excess of 100 degrees F. below zero. Even in summer the average monthly temperature at the south pole does not rise above zero. From our knowledge of the climates of the interiors of other continents, we should expect the interior of Antarctica to be "dry." This has not been clearly verified because of the difficulty of making precipitation measurements. There is abundant snow in the air on occasions, but it is not known whether this snow has fallen from the atmosphere and is precipitation, or whether it has been blown by the wind from somewhere else and is simply drift. However, the evidence indicates that actual snowfall is scant.

Between these two antarctic extremes we find variations and gradations. At Little America, a station on the edge of the Ross Ice Shelf where observations have been made for many years, we find a climate that is severe, yet milder than that of the interior. Here also precipitation is in doubt, although the accumulation of snow from unknown sources is very great.

Antarctica has long been seen in the role of a weather maker, the ice cap as a giant refrigeration machine with a limitless capacity for cooling the atmosphere. Cold air whirls off the continent in great spiral circulations known as anticyclones, which meet warmer, moister air lying over the adjacent oceans and create a belt of fog and snow and driving storms that have beset navigators from earliest times. Not for nothing have the high-latitude seas been called the "screaming sixties."

Antarctica without doubt has a part in world weather, even in the northern hemisphere, for billions of tons of cold air cannot be dumped into the rest of the atmosphere without effect. But the exact nature of the relationship

The arrows indicate the presumed circulation over Antarctica (shaded area). Down-moving currents over the polar region bring moisture-bearing air to the "giant refrigerating machine."

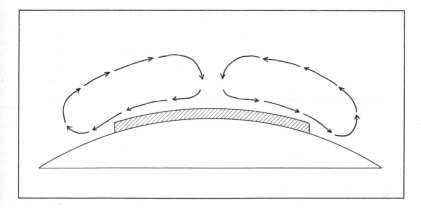

with the more northerly portions is not completely understood. For example, if air generally flows away from Antarctica, how does the snow which nourishes the ice cap
get to the interior? It is presumed that a southward movement of air in the upper atmosphere is responsible. But
this is not a certainty; it is not even a certainty that the
south pole gets much snow—if any. The scarcity of land
in the southern hemisphere from which to make observations, and the complete absence until recently of weather
data from the interior of the continent, have made these
particularly difficult problems. But now at long last the
necessary information is forthcoming (see Chapter 12) and
the matter is being sorted out. In the meantime there
are many better known vagaries of the weather which have
given Antarctica her notoriety and afford a view into her
temperament.

In Adelie Land the winds off the ice cap are so strong
a man can stand only by leaning. A simple walk outside
can become a struggle for survival. At Cape Denison,
where the Australian explorer Sir Douglas Mawson spent
two years, the average annual wind speed is the highest
found anywhere on the globe (48 mph). On many occasions his anemometers raced at ninety miles per hour
—ten miles per hour in excess of a standard hurricane.
For the month of May (1912) Mawson observed an average wind speed of 60.7 miles per hour, an experience
similar to sitting on the roof of a speeding car for four and
a half weeks.

Winds of such force have a special explanation. They
are called *katabatic winds* and consist of cold air spilling
down off the ice cap under the influence of gravity alone.
Cold air, more dense than overlying warm air, flows down-
hill, almost like water, gathering speed as it descends. In
Adelie Land the condition is enhanced by a long depres-

sion in the ice cap lying west of the Antarctic Horst and extending toward the pole. Into this natural flume the katabatic flow is funneled and gathers ever-greater speed as it plunges toward the coast. At the mouth of the flume, in the path of the snow-filled jet of air, stands Cape Denison. "The climate proved to be little more than one continuous . . . hurricane of wind for weeks together. . . . We had discovered an accursed country. . . . We had found the home of the blizzard."

In quieter moods the antarctic air has a distilled purity that exceeds the demands of the most exacting health faddist (or resort owner). It is dustless, germ free, and almost completely dry. It has a different chemical composition from temperate or tropical air, being slightly richer in nitrogen and the rare gas argon, and—though it hardly need be said—it has an invigorating artesian coolness that stirs even the most phlegmatic human organism.

On overcast days when the sky is milk white and blends indiscernibly with the snow-covered surface, we have the conditions necessary for *whiteout*. The horizon disappears; there are no shadows. The eye is bewildered and literally cannot tell up from down. Those who have experienced whiteout find it difficult to describe; those who have not find it difficult to believe. The explorer-geographer Dr. Paul Siple calls it the antithesis of darkness; he suggests it may be caused by the multiple reflections of light "trapped" between the layers of overcast and the surface. Airplane pilots say flying in a whiteout is like flying inside a ping-pong ball—or inside a bowl of milk. To these men it can be dangerous, especially during landings, when visual contact with the ground is necessary.

Again, when the air is still, we find what the meteorologist terms an *inversion,* a condition in which cold dense air lies close to the ground, warmer air above, and the usual conditions for vertical mixing are absent. It is this that the pioneers undoubtedly meant when they referred to the cold "lying like a blanket on the land." Inversions have an effect on the propagation of sound that causes the waves to hug the surface rather than bend upward and disappear as they do in temperate regions. In the antarctic men may carry on a conversation—if the inversion is intense—at a distance of a mile.

A layer of dense air next to the ground also does strange things to light, causing it to be refracted, or bent, unexpectedly. The sun may be visible long after it has set.

An antarctic snowscape; wind and drift obscure sky and horizon as a tractor train makes its way to an inland station.

Official U.S. Navy Photo

A *loomed* sun, it is called. Or land below the horizon may be subject to looming and made visible to a ship that ordinarily would be too far away to see it. This type of mirage caused some of the early explorers to make mistakes that were not easily explained. Another type stands ships upside down on their mastheads. Still another, caused not by inversion but by ice crystals suspended in the atmosphere, throws a halo around the sun or moon, or produces multiple suns (called parhelion) or multiple moons (called paraselene), or may simply cause a single moon to "make faces."

High up near the limits of the atmosphere, where the air is tenuous, occurs a phenomenon that lends Antarctica some of her haunting charm. This is the aurora australis, an incredibly thin veil of yellow (or greenish white or rose) light, darting, shimmering on the threshold of visibility, defying artist and photographer to capture it on paper. The evanescent display is a pale southern counterpart to the more brilliant and more familiar northern lights. Physicists believe it is caused by electrically charged particles which fly out into space from the sun and, in the vicinity of the earth, funnel down in the regions above the north and south magnetic poles. At heights of from sixty to two hundred miles the particles collide with oxygen and nitrogen atoms of the earth's atmosphere, causing these in turn to emit visible radiation.

But we have now got rather far ahead of the story. All these things about Antarctica which we accept so easily were once secrets wrested with only the greatest difficulty from that reluctant maiden. After Cook's illustrious voyage forty-five years passed before anyone discovered—or thought he had discovered—the last continent of adventure.

4

Sealers and Sailors

SOME TIME PRIOR to 1819 the news reached the maritime towns of New England that the valuable fur seal—seen and duly reported by Cook—abounded in the little known waters south of Cape Horn, and a fortune could be had simply for the taking. These were days of genuine Yankee enterprise, and many ships took up the call and headed south. Out of Stonington, Connecticut, sailed a fleet of five. The smallest vessel, the sloop *Hero,* was under the command of Nathanial Brown Palmer, then but twenty-one.

Within six months the boy-man would make his mark in history by sighting the antarctic continent and subsequently laying a claim to its discovery. This discovery would occupy us but briefly were it not that the matter is still unsettled. Many facts are at hand, and these are set forth as they are known today.

The sealing grounds were in the South Shetland Islands, which had been discovered by the English Captain William Smith, the first southern land to be found since Captain Cook had charted South Georgia in 1775. The Stonington fleet had been raised by the merchant trader Edward Fanning and was in command of Captain Benjamin Pendleton in the brig *Frederick.* The southing was made, and in November, 1820, all were at a curious anchorage which young Palmer had discovered in the *Hero.*

In ancient times a volcano had thrust itself above the surface of the sea, but now it was extinct. The sea had broached its rim and flooded its crater, forming a magnificent natural harbor ringed around with walls of old lava. Deception Island, it was appropriately named, possibly by Pendleton, who climbed up its black cinder slopes and spied a thin blue hint of land to the south. He sent young Nat Palmer to investigate.

Palmer was a tough, talented youth with a pleasant face and an excellent brain. He made his first sea voyage at fourteen, soon learned seamanship and navigation, and was mate and master by the time he was twenty. Such were his abilities that the Stonington owners did not hesitate to place him in command of his own ship for the six-thousand-mile voyage from New England to the antarctic.

No pictures of the *Hero* have survived, but we know from descriptions that she was a shallow-draft sloop less than fifty feet long. By present-day standards she might have made a lovely little cruising yacht, but the circumstances of the time made sailing in her a barely endurable hardship. She was solidly built, though with little regard for the comfort of the crew. Her spaces were small, there was no heat even for antarctic voyaging, and, inside, ice water steadily dripped down planks and bulkheads. It was intended that she act as a scout for the fleet, exploring unknown waters, discovering new beaches where seals might be found. She could also ferry sealskins from shoal waters which larger vessels could not enter.

The log book of the *Hero* is still in existence and may be examined in the Library of Congress. That there was something of the boy still in Palmer when he made his famous voyage, we may deduce from the little sailing ship which he skillfully drew on the canvas cover. Inside, the writing is neat and legible, though the entries are somewhat cryptic in their meaning.

Under November 16, 1820, appears the following: "Got underweigh; at 10 we were clear from the Harbor stood over for the Land Course S by E ½ E Ends with fresh Breezes and Pleasant." This is exactly as Palmer wrote it, and we may see that he was not too troubled by the rules of punctuation and grammar, yet the compact, run-together style may have been a deliberate attempt at a sort of shorthand necessary because of the cold and trying conditions in which the record had to be written.

The next day we find: "These 24 hours commence with fresh Breezes from the SWest and Pleasant at 8 P M got over under the Land found the sea was filled with imense Ice Bergs at 12 hove Too under the Jib Laid off & on until morning—at 4 A M made sail in shore and Discovered —a strait—Trending SSW & NNE—it was Literally filled with ice and the shore inaccessible we thought it not Prudent to Venture in ice Bore away to the Nothard & saw 2 small islands and the shore everywhere Perpendicular we stood across towards friesland Course NNW— the Latitude of the mouth of the strait was 63-45 S Ends with fine weather wind SSW."

It is puzzling stuff on which to base a claim for discovering a continent, but numerous experts, including Colonel Lawrence Martin of the Library of Congress, have concluded that all the evidence is there. Getting "under the land" refers to sailing past Trinity Island (see map), the "strait" is now called Orleans Channel, and the "inaccessible" shore was undoubtedly that of the antarctic mainland.

Captain Palmer left no other record, but shortly afterward a map appeared, drawn by the English Captain George Powell, on which the discovery was shown and called "Palmer's Land." The two captains had met at the sealing grounds the following year (1821), and Palmer gave sufficient information for the map to be drawn.

Did Palmer know that he had made a great discovery? There is no hint of it in the *Hero's* log, although in later years, after he had become a famous captain and builder of clipper ships, Palmer often stated that he had discovered Antarctica, and he was fond of telling the story of this arduous voyage of his youth. In 1820, however, he turned his back on the inaccessible shores and headed north to look for seals. He found them in abundance on the beaches of Greenwich Island.

When the Stonington fleet arrived in 1820, the number of fur seals was already thinning (see below), and rivalry especially between British and American vessels was keen. The search for new beaches was necessary and urgent, if the trade was to continue. Ships and crews occasionally met on less than friendly terms; there were arguments about priority on the beaches; outright battles were avoided only through extreme self-control. But Nat Palmer, with an openhandedness undoubtedly born of youth and optimism, maintained good relations at all times— including the strange occasion when he had an unexpected meeting with the Russian Captain Thaddeus von Bellingshausen.

It was two months after Palmer had made his discovery. The little *Hero* was drifting, surrounded by a fog, between the South Shetlands and the mainland. A ship's bell was heard, and then two ships loomed out of the cold murk, not sealers, but men of war flying the imperial Russian flag. A boat was lowered and Palmer joined Bellingshausen aboard the flagship for an exchange of information. The Russians were on an exploring expedition in the ships *Vostok* and *Mirny*, with the object of sailing around the world in a high southern latitude to discover antarctic lands. At the time of meeting, Bel-

Captain Nathaniel Brown Palmer. As a younger man he made explorations and discoveries in the antarctic regions.

lingshausen was of the opinion that his expedition had not yet sighted the mainland, although several offshore islands had been discovered, among them the Traverse Islands, Alexander Island, and Peter I Island.

This meeting at sea has a famous place in antarctic history, and much has been made of it by romancers. In one tale we hear of the Russian Commander "surrendering the palm" to young Nat and wailing, "What shall I tell my master?" This may now be written off as sheer invention. Palmer did not know the Russian language, Bellingshausen did not know English, and any conversation they engaged in must have been more awkward than this. The log of the *Hero* sheds no light on the matter, although the meeting is recorded in the log of the *Vostok,* which is preserved and was translated a number of years ago. Strangely, the meticulous Russian record does not mention Captain Palmer's discovery.

The Russian circumnavigation, begun in 1819 and completed in 1821, was a commendable piece of work which served to complement the earlier voyage of Captain Cook by filling in Cook's few gaps. It also held a long-hidden surprise. On February 15th and 18th, 1820, Bellingshausen saw "ice mountains" in latitude 69° south and 15° east, southeast of Cape Town, which he believed to be nothing more than huge icebergs floating in the sea.

As ice prevented a close approach, he sailed on. But a modern map shows that Bellingshausen was actually looking at the ice-encrusted mountains that lie behind the Princess Astrid Coast, and thus he had unknowingly discovered a section of the mainland. It has been argued that mistaking the identity of land and incorrectly calling it ice does not really constitute a "discovery." But the Soviet Union overlooks this and in a recent book we may read that the "honor of the Antarctic's discovery belongs, as everybody knows, to the Russian explorer Thaddeus Bellingshausen. . . ." If it were only that simple!

Among the many vessels that were in the South Shetlands region during the busy season of 1820 was the English brig *Williams,* under the command of Captain Edward Bransfield of the Royal Navy. Like Bellingshausen, Bransfield was an explorer intent on discovering new lands. Two accounts of the voyage were written afterward, but exact details pertaining to the ship's navigation and position are missing because the log has been lost. One important paper has survived, however, a chart of the voyage drawn in Captain Bransfield's own hand.

This document, which may be examined in the Hydrographic Department of the British Admiralty, shows a coastline trending roughly from southwest to northeast. Written along the coast are brief comments: "Supposed land: Lost in Fog," then "High Mountains covered with Snow," and finally "Here the coast was lined with Icebergs." On comparison with a modern chart it is quite clear that Captain Bransfield, in January, 1820, had discovered and sailed along the same coast which Captain Palmer sighted in November of the same year.

Geographers of the United States and England have settled a host of minor differences between them. But on the question of who discovered Antarctica and what the discovery is to be named, both sides have obstinately refused to yield an inch. The Americans have insisted that Palmer is the true discoverer and on their maps the peninsula, whose coast Palmer sighted, is named Palmer Peninsula in his honor. Bransfield probably made a voyage in the region, they say, but the absence of a log makes it impossible to base any claims to discovery on it.

The British believe that credit for the discovery properly belongs to Captain Bransfield, who sailed almost a

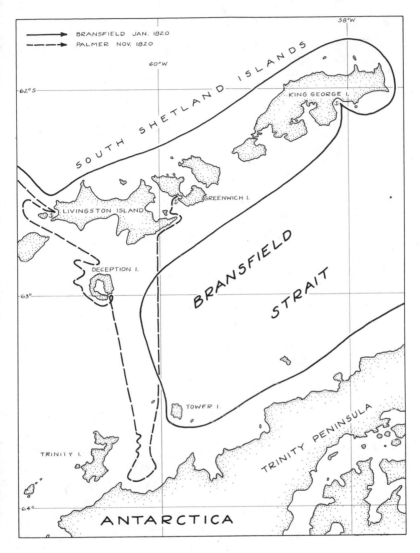

The discovery of Antarctica, 1820. For clarity, Palmer's return track is not shown.

year before Palmer and who left, if not a log book, another very clear record of his voyage. On their maps the peninsula in question is called Graham Land, after a lord of the Admiralty of that time. Captain Palmer undoubtedly made a voyage, they say, but it was *after* Bransfield's. In any case, the *Hero's* log is too vague a document on which to base a claim to an important discovery.

There the matter rests. At the present time evidence and opinion indicate that Captain Bransfield was the first to sight the antarctic mainland and that the world must one day recognize him. But attempts over the years to ennoble Nat Palmer have thoroughly obscured matters. And there has been no "official" recognition of this, for British and American maps continue their separate ways. In this book the name Palmer-Graham Land has been used, but this invention only pays respect to both camps and does not settle the question.

Recently Mr. Alexander Vietor of the Yale University Library has discovered an old log book which records an antarctic voyage of the New England sealer *Cecelia*. In February, 1821, her captain, John Davis, made a landing on the mainland, probably in the neighborhood of Hughes Bay. "I think," wrote Davis, "this Southern Land to be a Continent."

It was the first known landing on the continent, and its circumstances hold interesting implications. Sealers were trafficking in these waters as early as 1800, and as the competition increased the location of good sealing beaches was customarily kept secret. If the mainland *was* sighted during this early period, and if there were seals in abundance, the facts might have been concealed—and may yet come to light. The likelihood of this is not great; the supply of old log books is certainly not great. And smaller still is the chance that one of them contains an account of discovery. But it remains a tantalizing possibility.

The antarctic fur seal which so completely expropriated the thoughts and efforts of the Stonington men is a close relative of the northern fur seal which inhabits the Bering Sea and adjacent waters. As these northern animals had already been greatly reduced in numbers by Russian and American hunters, it was a stroke of good luck when Captain Cook reported the existence of a similar species in the antarctic. Within a few years of his return to England, the first adventurous northern sealers began poking into the far south. By 1820 the antarctic fleet numbered upward of fifty vessels, each on a ruthless search for fur.

The fur seal differs from other seals in having external ears, and for this reason it is also known as the eared seal. Occasionally it has been called the "sea bear," not entirely out of fancy, because zoologists consider the animal to be an offshoot of the bear family which took to an aquatic life in the remote past. The fur seal has a much greater flexibility of the hind flippers than other seals, giving it greater agility on land and lending it a remarkable resemblance to a four-footed animal encased in a sack. When properly prepared by tanning and removing the coarse outer protective hairs, the pelt of the animal becomes a soft, luxurious fur.

In the days of Pendleton and Palmer the fur was highly coveted by the wealthy mandarins of China, who were quite willing to pay exorbitant prices for it. So lucrative was the fur trade to China, a New England skipper could retire on the proceeds of a single voyage—if the hunting was good. This would require the taking of perhaps twenty to thirty thousand pelts within a period of two or three months, a task entirely possible in the early days of antarctic sealing. These could then be taken to Canton and sold or traded for goods worth $100,000 or more in the American market. No wonder Palmer and his men did not concern themselves with geography!

The antarctic fur seal spends most of the year in the water feeding on fish and mollusks. But during the brief summer months it sets itself upon a pilgrimage to land, crawling up, glistening and blinking, on the beaches of a multitude of antarctic islands. The beachmasters, ugly old males bearing the red and black scars of battles old and new, gather large harems, which they jealously defend against the advances of the younger "bachelors." It is a time of fighting and raucous bellowing, and also a time of tenderness. During this period the females (dubbed clapmatches by the sealers), give birth to a single pup— a simple ball of fur with button eyes, who is quickly taught to swim and is ready to strike out to sea in two months, when the summer ends.

In common with other antarctic animals, particularly the penguin, the seal has no enemy on shore and is completely fearless in the presence of man. This spelled doom for the fur seal. The sealers killed them simply by stepping ashore and striking the poor beasts on the head with a heavy club.

Occasionally there was a roar of protest and a half-hearted charge from an indignant bull. But this was easily remedied by gouging out one of his eyes and continuing the slaughter on his blind side. With the bull still "guarding" them, the females peacefully waited for the end. When a herd was found, every useful pelt was taken. The idea of conservation was unheard of. The naked carcasses were left to rot where they lay. The orphaned pups were left to starve. One can scarcely imagine the terrible scene the beaches must have presented after a visit by the sealers, or wonder that within an incredibly short time the antarctic fur seal was exterminated.

At least five other species of seal have managed to survive, however, and are found in the antarctic today. Of these the most interesting and preposterous is the elephant seal, a sea mammal which grows to be twenty feet long and thick enough in the middle to weigh five tons or more. Much of this enormous weight lies in a thick blanket of blubber which encases its body and protects its vital organs to some extent from the chill of the water. A charming feature is a trunk-like nose ten inches long and half as broad, which hangs down over the beast's mouth and inflates to twice its normal size during excitement or anger.

On land this grotesque seal is lethargic and nearly helpless, and completely ignorant of the danger of man. This resulted in its also being nearly exterminated during the last century, when the demand for oil for the industries of Europe and America was insatiable. The practice of the sealers was to invade the high tussock grass, a favorite haunt of the animal, shouting and swinging clubs until the unwilling creatures bestirred themselves and moved off to the beach. Here they were conveniently dispatched by a musket ball fired through the roof of the seal's mouth, a gruesome practice made necessary by the thickness of the skull, which resisted all efforts to smash it.

The blubber was then quickly stripped from the still-quivering beast and the oil rendered out in "try-pots," huge iron cauldrons set up on the beach and kept boiling over fires of fat-rich penguin carcasses. The smoke from this process was thick and black, besmirching everything within reach and making worse a business that was in itself bloody, greasy, and dirty.

The discovery of mineral oil in the ground and methods of refining it mercifully brought this phase of antarctic sealing to a conclusion. Though much reduced in numbers during their worst days, the elephant seal is now back in good strength, especially on the island of South Georgia, where it principally breeds and where British authorities have issued strict laws for its protection.

The other species of antarctic seal have never been of commercial value, but they have served as an important source of food, first for the sealers and then for explorers and their dogs. The Weddell seal, named after the man who first saw it, is a member of that far larger branch of the seal family known as the hair seals. These animals do

A herd of elephant seals on a beach in South Georgia, where they are protected from hunters by law.

Scott Polar Research Institute

not have real fur, they have no ears (only a pair of holes where ears should be), and their hind flippers extend stiffly to the rear and are of no use in progression on land or ice.

Out of the water, hair seals are clumsy and helpless, especially the Weddell, which attains a length of ten feet and a weight of eight hundred pounds. Its coat has a lovely mottled pattern, and it has a soft brown-eyed face that has been called "friendly." Its home is in the water at the edge of the pack, although in summer it crawls up on the ice and appears to spend much of its time dozing and basking in the sun.

The crabeater seal is a smaller relative, more lithe and active, subsisting for the most part on bottom-living crustaceans. The hair-seal family also has a predaceous member, the leopard seal. This twelve-foot creature is the water-dwelling counterpart of the jungle cat after which it was named. Strong and supple, spotted around the shoulders, and armed with sharp carnivorous teeth, it preys on penguins and other seals.

Some authorities state that the leopard seal will attack man unequivocally, but as antarctic waters offer little inducement to bathing, there is little evidence to support this. On the other hand, the hardy English zoologist Harry R. Lillie is of the opinion that the leopard seal is entirely harmless and that a swimming party with him, if you could endure the cold, would be great fun. However, this is a modern opinion, and many years were to pass before Antarctica and her seals were looked upon with anything but hostility.

5

Magnetism, Fire, and Ice

THE UNVEILING of Antarctica was a protracted process.
Of the more than three hundred voyages made to antarctic waters during the 19th Century, most were in
search of seals and whales. Only three were purely scientific enterprises with the specific purpose of exploring
the continent in a methodical way.

One was an American expedition led by Naval Lieutenant Charles Wilkes. It was a disastrous semi-failure that
caused Wilkes to be held in disrepute for many years.
Another was French, led by Jules Sebastien Cesar Dumont
D'Urville; it achieved a fleeting rendezvous with the continent which survives on the map as Adelie Land. The
third was British; it was led by Sir James Clark Ross, who
had the unusual reputation of being the handsomest man
in the British Navy. All three returned with convincing
evidence that a land mass of continental proportions did
lie within the armored fortress of the ice pack.

In fairness to poor Wilkes it must be stated that he was
a dedicated and honest man who was victimized by circumstances. Through no fault of his own he sailed in
ships ill-founded and half rotten; one vessel was lost with
all hands, the crews of the remainder were miserable
throughout the voyage. His numerous discoveries along
the coast of what is now called Wilkes Land were made
during conditions of mirage, which caused his charts to
contain serious errors. Explorers who followed could not
find the discoveries in question, and Wilkes was quickly
branded a liar.

Matters have since been set right; mirages are well understood, the landfalls made by Wilkes have been recognized and put on the map, his reputation has been restored. But the incident was an unpleasant one and a reason why the United States Government shunned antarctic exploration for a hundred years.

At the same time that Wilkes and D'Urville were making their preparations, the British Association for the Advancement of Science determined that an attempt should be made to reach the south magnetic pole, which was thought to lie within the antarctic circle. Since Ross had already distinguished himself by leading an expedition to the north magnetic pole, and had other high qualifications, it was imperative that he be chosen to lead the new search.

Unlike Wilkes, Ross had the finest equipment. His ships *Erebus* and *Terror* were heavily built bombardment vessels further strengthened and reinforced to withstand the expected rough usage. The crews' quarters were carefully weatherproofed; food and clothing were of the best quality obtainable. There was a variety of scientific and magnetic instruments, including the simple but necessary dip circle with which the magnetic pole would be located.

The south magnetic pole is one of the two points toward which the ends of a compass needle point, the other being the more familiar north magnetic pole in the arctic regions. This is a consequence of the earth itself's behaving like a big magnet in space. Both magnetic poles are several hundred miles distant from their respective geographical poles which mark the ends of the axis of rotation, and thus a compass needle rarely indicates the direction true north or true south.

At the south geographic pole the south end of a compass needle will point in the direction of the south magnetic pole—which is to the north! It is clear that a navigator in the vicinity of *any* of the poles must thoroughly understand his compass, although at the present time this instrument has been supplanted by the gyrocompass and sun compass, which are more accurate and reliable.

In the immediate vicinity of a magnetic pole the magnetic compass becomes sluggish and erratic, but a magnetized needle free to turn vertically, as in the dip circle, points directly downward. The daily fluctuations of the earth's magnetic field and the slow drift of the magnetic poles from year to year are added complications. These facts are well known now and understood even by a good many schoolboys. However, when Ross sailed in 1839, terrestrial magnetism was an undeveloped science; the south magnetic pole was unknown, its existence and location had been surmised only on theoretical grounds by the German mathematician Carl Friedrich Gauss.

Ross crossed the antarctic circle near the 180th meridian. Intermittent gales tossed his small ships, blowing whales disported about them during calms, and icebergs constantly threatened, especially during mists, when the only warning of their approach was the sound of waves dashing against their sides. Some of these were flat-topped giants, rising sheer-walled a hundred fifty feet above the water, implying depths of seven times that below the surface.

They moved slowly, defying the wind and leaving a wake of boiling chips and fragments like the ermine of a monarch's train. Ross speculated on their origin, for no glaciers in Greenland, with which he was familiar, could have produced such masses of ice. As his ships continued southward, scattered bergs were joined by drifting fields of sea ice. Then at last the grinding pack was met. It had turned back Cook, held off D'Urville, and confounded Wilkes. But Ross had good fortune; in four days he was *through* it, and beyond lay a clear sea to the south.

Ross steered for the magnetic pole, confident that the open water of the Ross Sea (subsequently named after him) would lead him directly to it. The behavior of the dip needle, now only five degrees from the vertical, and the variation of the standard compass were evidence that he was very close. Early on the morning of January 11, 1840, progress to the south was halted, not by ice, but by land rising on the horizon. During the day the distance to the shore was closed, but a landing was prevented by ice.

This was solid antarctic land, not the misty glimpses caught by Bransfield and Palmer, not the mirage-ridden coast of Wilkes, but a real land of dark-colored sunlit rock etched against blue sky with the sharpness of a copperplate engraving. ". . . We had a most enchanting view of . . . two magnificent ranges of mountains, whose lofty peaks, perfectly covered with eternal snow, rose to elevations varying from seven to ten thousand feet above the level of the ocean. The glaciers that filled the intervening valleys, which descended from near the mountain summits, projected in many places several miles into the sea, and terminated in lofty perpendicular cliffs. . . ."

The new coastline trended to the south. As Ross sailed along it, peak after peak rose to view, and to the most imposing he gave the names of the lords of the Admiralty who had planned and provided for the expedition. Ross was not the first to use personal names for the geographical features of the antarctic, but the extensive landfall enabled him to do so with a generous hand.

Explorers who followed saw no reason to change the

agreeable custom. As a result the map of Antarctica is a fantastic directory of names—of explorers, their wives, their sons and daughters, their friends and benefactors, their kings and emperors, their princes and princesses. Only recently have geographical councils ruled that the names of pets and proprietary products shall not be used!

Two weeks later Ross saw a new high land in latitude 77° south. On close approach in clear weather ". . . it proved to be a mountain twelve thousand four hundred feet of elevation above the level of the sea, emitting flame and smoke in great profusion." It was an active volcano, and Ross attached great significance to such a discovery in the antarctic, expecting it to throw further light on the physical construction of the globe.

This expectation has not been fully realized, for even today earth scientists do not have a complete understanding of the role of volcanoes in the history of the earth's crust. It is a familiar fact that the Pacific Ocean is surrounded by a belt of mountains and active volcanoes. The earthquakes of Japan and California, the eruptions in the East Indies and South America are evidence of this.

It has been suggested that the "ring of fire" is a line of weakness in the earth's crustal rocks, a wound left by the terrible cataclysm that occurred when the material now comprising our moon was wrenched from the planet, leaving behind a great basin which has become the Pacific Ocean. This startling hypothesis is not entirely acceptable to all scientists, some of whom see the moon formed in another way and the ring of fire caused by another agent. Whatever the explanation, Antarctica will be a part of it. Ross's volcano is in the ring of fire, as is Deception Island, the volcanic remnant in West Antarctica.

Ross named the peak Mount Erebus, after his ship. A

smaller inactive cone nearby was named after the *Terror*.
Progress to the south being blocked by these new discoveries, Ross turned his ships to the east. Presently
". . . we perceived a low white line extending . . . as
far as the eye could discern to the eastward. It presented
an extraordinary appearance, gradually increasing in
height as we got nearer to it, and proving at length to be
a perpendicular cliff of ice between one hundred fifty
and two hundred feet above the level of the sea, perfectly
level and flat at the top. . . . It is impossible to conceive
a more solid looking mass of ice; not the smallest rent or
fissure could we discover throughout its whole extent, and

Mount Erebus, antarctic volcano first seen by Ross, a link
in the "ring of fire."

Official U.S. Navy Photo

the intensely bright sky beyond it but too plainly indicated the great distance to which it reached to the southward. . . ."

For 300 miles Ross sailed cautiously along the "great
icy barrier," sometimes standing out to sea to avoid being
dashed against it by the waves, sometimes sailing close to
gaze in wonderment at the sheer ice walls, here standing
out in buttresses, there hollowed like a blue cathedral,
and everywhere glistening and murmuring from the
countless cascades of melting water tumbling down and
across its face. Soundings made along the barrier showed
the sea to have a depth of 1600 to 2400 feet, and Ross
concluded that the ice was afloat and possessed a below-
water depth of approximately a thousand feet. Such a mass
of ice was new in the experience of man. When Ross returned to England, the barrier was accepted as his greatest
discovery—although he brought back other things valuable to science. And in the more than one hundred years
that have elapsed since that time the barrier has never
ceased to be an object of amazement and study.

Ross's "barrier" was in reality the seaward edge of an
ice shelf. He used the term barrier for the good reason
that it absolutely blocked the way of his ships and, in his
view, all future ships, to the south. Had he some small
inkling of the extent of the ice beyond the high wall over
which he could not see, he might have hit upon the term
shelf, which modern geographers have adopted as more
descriptive. Of all the many ice shelves scattered around
the edges of Antarctica the Ross Ice Shelf (also named
after him) is by far the largest.

From its seaward edge it extends more than four hundred miles to the mountains of the Great Antarctic Horst.
Its maximum width is 500 miles; its area is about 160,000
square miles. Recent precise measurements of its thick-

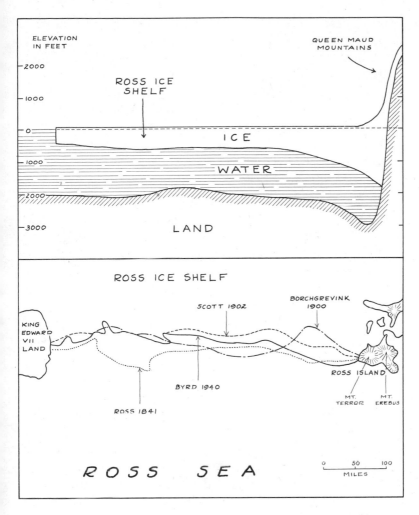

The Ross Ice Shelf. Top: Profile along the 170th meridian showing that the shelf is largely afloat; the vertical scale is exaggerated. Bottom: Changes in the position of the edge of the shelf during the past century. (After Kosack)

ness range from 790 to 1050 feet. The upper surface has an average elevation of 170 feet above sea level and is remarkably even, varying less than sixty feet between high and low spots.

The shelf is aground in a number of places, notably on Roosevelt Island near the eastern end of its edge. But because of the plasticity of the ice, the effects of the groundings are local, and the main mass of the shelf may be considered to be afloat. Near the sea it rises and falls a few feet with the tide, and this causes the breaking off of the tabular bergs first observed by Ross. Thirty miles back from the edge no vertical movement at all has been detected. In the same manner as a land glacier, the ice shelf moves seaward at a rate of about five miles per year.

The attendant calving of bergs keeps the ice front more or less stationary, although there have been differences of twenty miles or more in the position of the ice front over periods of several years, and there is evidence of a general retreat of the front since its discovery in 1840. All statistics aside, the Ross Ice Shelf may be visualized as an ice raft as big as France and thick enough to contain the Empire State Building standing upright.

Professor R. F. Flint of Yale University believes that the Ross Ice Shelf was formed, at least in the initial stages, by the large glaciers which pour down from the Antarctic Horst, and in the east, where the relief is low, by the direct flow of the inland ice cap. This comprises an enormous ingress of ice, but it is insufficient to have built up and maintained the present thickness of the shelf. This has probably been accomplished by the accumulation of snow and the development of firn in the same manner as that which forms a land glacier.

In ancient times the shelf may have been much thinner, even of a ribbed appearance when the outflowing valley glaciers dominated its structure. As the firn developed, its thickness increased until isostatic forces within the plastic floating mass brought it to a uniform thickness with a smooth and nearly level top surface. (Isostasy is nothing more than Archimedes' principle of flotation applied to very large objects. It can be demonstrated with a bowl of water which has a layer of sawdust floating on the surface. Added sawdust does not accumulate in a pile; it simply causes a general rearrangement of all the particles, resulting in an increased but still uniform thickness of the floating layer.)

At present the Ross Ice Shelf is thought to be in a state of equilibrium, the accretion of firn on the top surface being exactly balanced by the melting at the lower surface caused by contact with the relatively warm sea water. Individual ice particles are thus subject to two movements, one in the direction of the sea, one downward—but both toward destruction.

The snow accumulation on the surface is about sixteen inches per year. This figure is arrived at by studying the records of the explorer Richard Byrd, who occupied a series of camps in the same general location on the ice shelf over a period of twenty-five years. Each successive camp was built on top of the previous one, which had become completely buried by snow. Growing at this speed, the only surprise is that the shelf, which is certainly many thousands of years old, is not thicker than it is. Ignorant of its true nature, Ross nevertheless was able to observe, ". . . a mighty and wonderful object, far beyond anything we could have thought or conceived."

The season was waning, and Ross thought it prudent to turn away from his extraordinary discovery and make for Australia. He knew now that the magnetic pole could not be reached by ship. (It was not until 1909 that the

Australian explorer Sir T. E. Edgeworth David fixed its position then in latitude 72° south and longitude 115° east. Since that time it has drifted some four hundred miles and is presently in the region of 68° south and 144° east. Professor David was a remarkable man who took up antarctic exploring at the age of fifty. Among his accomplishments was the first ascent of Mount Erebus and the exploration of its cone.)

Ice and mountains had contrived to bar Ross from the magnetic pole, but his failure was slight, in view of his discoveries. Perhaps his greatest was the open sea he found south of the pack. The Ross Sea and the Ross Ice Shelf lying behind it appear as a broad smooth road to the interior of the continent. In the next era of antarctic exploration, in which we turn from science to adventure and heroism, they proved to be so.

6

To the Uttermost Point

ROBERT F. SCOTT had no intention of becoming a hero. He professed no interest in the antarctic world. He was bent on a career in the British Navy. But as luck frequently has it, he was there when someone was wanted, and he possessed outstanding qualities: a strong but inscrutable character, an inquiring mind, and that trait encountered again and again in the exploring breed, an implacable determination to get a thing done and to drive and drive and never quit until it is done.

There was also a hint of drama in Scott's make-up, for he had a thoughtful, inward-turning manner which earned him the nickname "Old Moony" while still at school. The choice of Scott as leader of two British antarctic expeditions (the first the "National" expedition of 1901 and the second a private enterprise of 1911), was a continuation of the successful tradition begun with Cook of looking to the Navy for the leadership of scientific expeditions.

The main objectives were ostensibly scientific, and both efforts yielded volumes of data unequaled at that time and still a source of information about the antarctic. But behind this lay another, more exciting, goal: the south pole, the uttermost point of the earth, a fascination to the mind of man ever since it was known that the earth was a sphere. Scott was determined that the British should reach the south pole first.

In this regard the first expedition was a failure. Only the feeblest efforts were made in the direction of the pole. This was not a discredit to Scott, for he was a pioneer, the first to attempt to travel and explore into the interior, the first to cope with the problems of surface transport far from a ship. The Eskimo-type sledge had been settled on as a suitable vehicle, but the ideal means of drawing it had not yet been found—at least not by the British.

Scott had had some experience with the Eskimo dog and included several teams in his outfit, but he had little faith in their abilities in the colder and more severe climate of the south. He strongly disliked the overworking, under-feeding, and killing of dogs necessary on long hard journeys. "In my mind," Scott stated, "no journey ever made with dogs can approach the height of that fine conception which is realized when a party of men go forth to face hardships, dangers, and difficulties with their own unaided efforts. . . ." In the kit of every trail party, therefore, were a number of harnesses for the *manhauling* of sledges. This romantic notion ultimately cost Scott his life.

His base for the second attempt was at Hut Point on Ross Island, where stand Mounts Erebus and Terror, dis-covered by Scott's compatriot half a century before. It has been a favorite corner of the antarctic for British, and lately American, explorers. There is ice-free water close to shore and ice-free ground on which to erect buildings.

The sterile cold of the antarctic is an excellent preserver, and Scott's timber hut still stands, bleak and weather worn, filled with accumulated ice and abandoned memo-rabilia, half morbid, half poignant. It has been visited and photographed by recent expeditions and has attained the hallowed status of an historic shrine. But in 1911 its walls rang with British optimism. Rations were being packed, trail gear weighed for the journey ahead.

Scott's route was clear: across the Ross Ice Shelf, through the mountains of the Horst by way of the Beardmore Glacier, then over the polar plateau to the pole. The total distance out and back: 1700 miles. It was the "British" route discovered and pioneered by Ernest Shackleton in 1908 (see Chapter 7).

Scott had greatly improved his equipment and techniques, but in the matter of transport he again misjudged, passing over the known advantages of Eskimo dogs and choosing to have his sledges hauled in the initial stages by Siberian and Manchurian ponies. These tough stubborn animals from the steppes of central Asia were known to possess almost unbelievable endurance in cold and blizzard. But they had already been tried by Shackleton who formed the opinion that dogs would have been better.

The ponies did not thrive. During the long ocean voyage to the south two died; after disembarking in the antarctic six perished on a disastrous journey across the ice of McMurdo Sound, another sickened and died mysteriously. On the eve of the great southern journey only eight remained of the original nineteen. But Scott was convinced that if these survivors could take him through the mountains, manhauling would get him the rest of the way. On November 11, five weeks after the first day of antarctic spring, sixteen men, the ponies, thirteen sledges, and an aggregate load of 7000 pounds of food, fuel, and gear started south—a bizarre caravan, muffled against the cold, creeping slowly, silently across the white desert.

In the early stages Scott was accompanied by supporting parties whose function was to lay down depots of food and supplies which would be picked up on the return. As distances out increased, supporting parties turned back, leaving a reduced number to carry on to the next stage. It was a complicated mode of advance dictated by the utter barrenness of the antarctic countryside which provides not one atom for the traveler.

Progress was made. Mile by mile, day by day, Scott and his company moved across the plain. The ponies proved a miserable failure, all dying or having to be shot because of illness, before the mountains were reached. The ascent of the Beardmore, which Scott had hoped would be aided by the ponies, was a grueling job of man-hauling.

In latitude 87° 35' south the last supporting party made ready to turn back. Scott was in a weak position for a dash to the pole. The weather had been bad, the hauling surfaces worse. The journey was behind schedule, and food supplies were already short. A faint-hearted man would have turned back. A thoughtful one would have hesitated. Scott not only chose to go on, but he compounded the coming tragedy by increasing the size of the party heading for the pole from four—as planned from the outset—to five.

Lieutenant E. R. G. R. Evans, later Admiral Lord

Beardmore Glacier, largest valley glacier in the world. Discovered by Shackleton, used by Scott, it was the "British route" to the pole.

U.S. Air Force Photo

Mountevans, who led the return party, wrote, "We shook hands all round, and we felt very moved as we looked into their eyes. . . . There were cakes of ice on their beards, weather scars, split lips, frostbite marks . . . the last we saw was a tiny black speck on a great white horizon of ice. From the time we left them an evil spirit seemed to dog Scott's footsteps."

In the pole party, besides Scott, were Dr. Edward Wilson, scientist and watercolorist, Lt. Henry R. Bowers of the Royal Indian Marines—short in stature but with great physical reserves and incredible vision—Petty Officer Edgar Evans, who possessed great size and strength, and Captain L. E. G. Oates, a quiet aristocrat who represented the Army. Scott was 43, Wilson 39, the rest in their twenties.

The evil spirits which dogged Scott were rotten weather and poor surfaces. Temperatures were unexpectedly low and frequent blizzards made it necessary to hole up in the tents, consuming valuable time and eating precious food without making any advance. Scott's diary contains frequent references to the loose, sugary texture of the snow that made sledge hauling twice the work anticipated.

"We stuck ten yards from camp," Bowers recorded in his diary, "and nine hours later found us little more than half a mile on. . . . I have never pulled so hard, or so nearly crushed my inside into my backbone by the everlasting jerking against the canvas band. . . ." Nonetheless the gap was closed, and on January 16th (1912) the pole was only twenty-four miles away.

Eagle-eyed Bowers spotted a black speck on the horizon which seemed not a part of the natural landscape. On closer approach it proved to be a small black cloth flag stuck up on a sledge member. Farther on, one and a half miles from the south pole, were a tent and messages. One was to the Norwegian king, Haakon VII; a second was

to Scott himself. Both were signed by the Norwegian
explorer Roald Amundsen, who had reached the pole a
month before.

For the five Englishmen it was a dark moment. There
was no triumph, no joy, only mocking disappointment.
The eight hundred hard-won miles, the great labors, the
high risks, were obviously in vain. "The Pole," wrote
Scott. "Yes, but under very different circumstances from
those expected. . . ."

It did not come as a complete surprise. Scott had known
months before that he would have a rival in the south.
He had simply hoped, against probabilities, that he would
not be beaten. It was not to be a race, Scott insisted. But
it *was* a race, and the other man was a tough veteran, not
to be beaten by hopes alone.

In many respects Amundsen was Scott's direct opposite.
He was dynamic, aggressive, cunning—some have said
ruthless. He made his name as an explorer in the arctic.
He used Eskimo dogs and adopted other Eskimo methods.
He had a marvelous flair for fast polar travel. And there
was a certain sly humor about him, for when he stood at
the south pole he considered it slightly mad, since most of
his life he had dreamed of going to the north pole.

Amundsen's expedition had, in fact, originally been
planned to take him to the north pole, but when the
American explorers Cook and Peary reached the vicinity
of this point in 1908 and 1909, he saw that the challenge
was gone, and he secretly changed his plans. He felt secrecy
was necessary to prevent his backers and his men from
losing faith in him. But the secrecy clouded his reputation,
and in the end he felt compelled to announce his intention
to Scott, after all.

Explorers endure hardship and suffering to increase
the bulk of human knowledge, and for this reason can

perhaps be forgiven their idiosyncrasies. Scott possessed an exaggerated sense of sportsmanship. He had announced his plan of going to the pole, and he expected others to avoid scrupulously making similar plans until he had had his try. Amundsen obstinately refused to agree with this view. The pole belonged to no one, and would be claimed by the first man with the stamina and know-how to get there. Who could say, either before or after the tragic events which followed, that one view was right and the other wrong?

Amundsen built his base on the Bay of Whales, not a real bay but an indentation in the Ross Ice Shelf which Scott had discovered a decade before. This was a bold move (typical of Amundsen), for the cautious view (typical of Scott) held that the constant calving of huge bergs from the edge of the shelf would make the Bay of Whales unsafe for the location of a winter camp. But Amundsen reasoned that if the bay had persisted as a feature of the ice front for ten years, it would persist for another ten months. He reasoned correctly, and in so doing placed himself sixty miles nearer the pole than Scott, with a smoother road to travel.

If Scott's was a journey in which everything seemed to go wrong, Amundsen's was one in which everything went right. The Norwegian plan was generally the same as the English. The main advance was to be supported by depots previously laid out. But where Scott used ponies, Amundsen used dogs. And it may also have been significant that, where Scott's men wore woolens and windproofs, Amundsen's party were clad in thick reindeer fur. After a false start in September, which failed because of brutal cold —temperatures as low as 75° below zero—the southern journey was begun on October 20th, still three weeks earlier than Scott's.

Amundsen's party consisted of five men, four sledges, fifty-two dogs, and enough provisions for four months. "Everything was in order, and we had made up our minds to take it easy during the first part of the journey. . . ." The tone of Amundsen's record is one of confidence and efficiency. He planned to travel no more than eighteen miles a day, but this proved too little "thanks to our strong and willing animals." Contrast this with the bedeviled British, who were breaking their backs to cover half a mile in a morning. Frequently Amundsen's dogs pulled the heavily laden sledges more than thirty miles in a twenty-four-hour period.

The Norwegians penetrated the Queen Maud Mountains (eastern end of the Horst) by way of the Axel Heiberg Glacier, 150 miles east of Scott's route. The country was treacherous, uphill and full of crevasses. But the dogs were flexible, and in the worst places twenty were hitched to a single sledge and the advance made in relays. In four days Amundsen climbed from the ice shelf to the polar plateau, a rise of over 7000 feet in a distance of 120 miles —an incredible display of speed and efficiency. And here came the odious task of killing twenty-four of the brave dogs that had made the feat possible.

On a journey such as this the load on the outward leg is necessarily greater than on the return. Some supplies, particularly food, are used up, and others are left in depots to be used on the way back. Thus the large number of animals needed to haul the heavy outgoing loads are not required on the return. If they are to be kept they must be fed, and this means additional weight in food that must be handled and hauled all round. The simple and obvious expedient is to destroy the dogs when they have reached the end of their usefulness. Not only is the extra hauling eliminated, but the meat of the slaughtered animals is good food for the survivors, and still more haulage is saved.

Aside from the cold efficiency of such a system, a very real benefit is the reduction in risk to the lives of the human members of the party. Whether or not the practice is cruel, whether or not it is necessary, are questions that must be settled in one's own mind.

Once on the plateau, Amundsen's way to the pole was clear, the journey almost without event. The dogs literally raced, and the miles clicked off on the sledge meters. On December 16th the pole was reached. A series of meticulous observations were made to verify the position. The next day Amundsen was ready to go again. The homeward journey was made at an average speed of 22½ miles per day. The party arrived back at their base on January 25th with two sledges, eleven dogs, and "all well."

Amundsen's journey has a firm place in polar history. It is a classical example of efficiency and practical skill. But it stands in the shadow of Scott's fate. The latter, one month behind his rival, could not remotely dream of the ease with which the great prize had been taken from him.

There is no doubt that Scott and his men were disappointed. It is less clear if this mood hindered their subsequent efforts. What remained was an eight-hundred-mile slog home, no journey to tackle in an unsettled state of mind. And what a terrible journey it proved to be, a nightmare of bad weather and five brave men, already weakened by short rations, standing up to knife-edged winds with temperatures going down to forty and fifty below. Thick blizzards again pinned them down, reducing a very narrow margin of safety until there was none, and Scott pondered whether they would get through at all.

In descending the Beardmore Glacier, Seaman Evans,

numbed with cold, lagged behind, stumbled and fell a dozen times, rose to struggle on in a daze. On February 17th he collapsed and died from exhaustion and exposure. It was a dreadful turn of events. If Evans, the biggest and strongest of the party, could not survive, what of the rest?

The cold was severely felt by every man. Faces were raw from frostbite, fingers and feet ached constantly. Food was frightfully short, stomachs gnawed and eyes gleamed. Scott wrote one night, "We camped with great difficulty . . . we were dreadfully cold . . . everyone's feet cold . . . Oates' feet very cold."

In early March Oates began to lag. His feet were now quite frozen and every step brought excruciating pain.

Scott's party at the pole, cold and haggard, facing cruel journey home. From left: Oates, Bowers, Scott, Wilson, Evans.

For many days the brave man struggled on in silent agony, sometimes crawling the last few yards to the tent at the end of a day's march. The others, in desperate physical straits themselves, could offer little help. On March 14th Oates saw that he had reached the end; he hoped to die in his sleep that night, but he awoke the next morning. Outside, a blizzard was blowing. Oates left the tent, walked out into the storm and was never seen again. He sacrificed himself in order that his comrades in distress might survive. ". . . It was the act of a brave man and an English gentleman."

Hope for those remaining lay in reaching a depot known as One Ton Camp. Here were abundant food and fuel. Here also should be a welcoming party from the base. But One Ton Camp was twenty miles away and Scott was many days behind his schedule.

Cold, starved, exhausted, the three men had struggled to within eleven miles of the depot when another blizzard pinned them down. Food was gone. Strength ebbed fast. And here the end came. "Outside the door of the tent it remains a scene of whirling drift. I do not think we can hope for any better things now. We shall stick it out to the end, but we are getting weaker . . . and the end cannot be far. It seems a pity, but I do not think I can write more. R. Scott."

Eight months later a search party from the base at Hut Point found them, lying as if in sleep, Scott with his arm about his friend Wilson. He had been the last to die; though the oldest, his heart had proved the strongest. Beside him were his diaries and journals, photographs, scientific records, geological specimens. They had stuck to everything to the very last, and it told the whole terrible story.

It is hardly credible that the snuffing out of five promis-

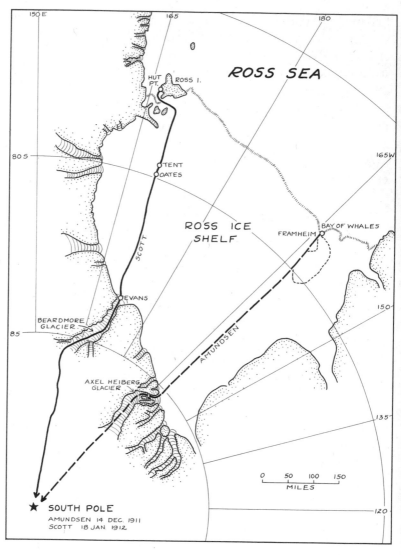

150 E   165   180

ROSS SEA

165 W

HUT
PT.   ROSS I.

80 S

TENT
OATES

ROSS ICE
SHELF

BAY OF WHALES
FRAMHEIM

150

SCOTT

EVANS

BEARDMORE
GLACIER

AMUNDSEN

85

AXEL HEIBERG
GLACIER

135

0   50   100   150
MILES

120

★ SOUTH POLE
AMUNDSEN 14 DEC. 1911
SCOTT 18 JAN. 1912

Journeys to the uttermost point, 1911-12, ending in
triumph and tragedy.

ing lives could afford any benefit to even the small world of explorers and scientists, yet Scott's last tragic expedition was not without results. There was of course the scientific material produced by other members of the staff —physicists, meteorologists, biologists, photographer, and other specialists. Their results were of as much value as had been expected, and are still in use today.

But Scott's polar journey had other lessons to offer. Ponies were no good in the antarctic, and manhauling was worse. A late start means a late finish, accompanied by the bad weather of autumn; this was a second major factor in Scott's failure. Woolen clothing is probably not as good as fur. If plans are changed midway (adding Oates to the polar party), it is better to change in the direction of greater safety than greater risk.

In the antarctic the big strong man (such as Seaman Evans) does not have the last-ditch resistance of the smaller, more wiry man (such as Bowers and Scott). All these matters were taken into consideration by later explorers, and never forgotten when their minds were put to solving further antarctic problems. The great pity was that the cost of learning these lessons had been so high.

7

Trial and Tribulation

A LITTLE BIT of hero business goes a long way, especially in a world where there is a tendency to blow things up to twice life size. But the antarctic is a world apart, and it has produced more genuine heroes than are dreamed of. Not all can be mentioned in this book, but some cannot be omitted. Scott is one. Ernest Shackleton is another. But where Scott's story stirs the heart, Shackleton's stirs the blood. Getting out of a tight corner was his specialty.

He was not a promising boy, at least in the manner that most boys show promise, for at school he was definitely not outstanding. He was shy as well. And when his name was in the headlines on six continents, friends of his youth tried in vain to remember some quality of Shackleton the boy that would explain the extraordinary qualities of Shackleton the man and antarctic explorer.

It may have been that he was a hopeless romantic. To him exploring was a fabulous game. He freely admitted that he was not in it for science, although he always took along a few members of that tribe to satisfy his backers. No, he was in it for personal glory and riches, which is closer to the truth than most others would care to admit about themselves. Shackleton was never dull, he was frequently daring, and sometimes he was dangerous.

In 1908 he mounted his first antarctic expedition. He was not a novice to exploration, for he had been with Scott on the unsuccessful attempt to reach the pole in 1902. (It is interesting to observe how in a given period of exploration the careers of men are intertwined.) But

Scott's somewhat methodical manner was not amenable to Shackleton's more energetic nature, and he determined to explore on his own. His object was the pole and little else.

Shackleton placed his base at Cape Royds on Ross Island. This caused embarrassment, since Captain Scott was obsessed with the idea that no one else should make a base in this area until he himself had made another attempt for the pole. Shackleton agreed to respect this attitude and planned to put his camp on the Bay of Whales—before Amundsen thought of it—but sea ice prevented a landing. He rushed then to Cape Royds, breaking his word to Scott out of dire necessity. Nonetheless, this provoked Scott, who never spoke to Shackleton again.

Shackleton made a splendid journey. He pushed beyond Scott's old farthest south, penetrating the western ranges of the Antarctic Horst. He discovered and ascended the Beardmore Glacier—the largest valley glacier in the world, ten miles wide, one hundred twenty miles long, a magnificent but treacherous highway to the polar plateau. Shackleton reached the plateau. He was the first man to do so, the first to experience the sublime desolation of this uttermost region of the earth. But he did not make the pole.

At a point 137 miles away, a shortage of food forced him to decide that he must turn back here or not return at all. On January 9, 1909, after seventy-three days of tough slogging, the last sixty hours of which were solid blizzard, he wrote, "Our last day outwards. We have shot our bolt and the tale is 88° 23' south. . . . Whatever regrets may be, we have done our best."

Time worked against Shackleton, and the pole was reached before he could raise another expedition. He did not despair, for his mind had already settled on a new journey, twice as long, twice as daring, and only half possible. He proposed crossing Antarctica from coast to coast, passing the pole on the way. He saw in such a trek fresh excitement, new glories. Three-quarters of the route lay in unknown country; he would penetrate it and see for the first time the heart of the antarctic.

Armchair explorers were of the opinion that the journey was too difficult, that certain loss of life threatened— and with some justification, for the memory of Scott was still vivid. But Shackleton found backers. "No matter how fantastic the plan," an associate said, "when Shackleton described it, you *believed* in it!"

There were to be two ships. The *Endurance,* a sailing vessel with auxiliary steam, newly fitted out for polar work, would penetrate the Weddell Sea and land a party on Caird Coast. The second ship, *Aurora,* would land another party in the McMurdo Sound area on the opposite side of the continent. Traveling by dog team, the two would head for the pole, meet somewhere on the plateau, and finish "the last grand journey" together. It is something to say for Shackleton's vision and audacity that forty years were to elapse before men and machines were equal to the plan.

During the first century of antarctic exploration the Weddell Sea appeared so ice-jammed and impenetrable that James Weddell, who sailed into it in 1822, was politely called a liar. In 1903 the ship *Antarctic* of the Swedish expedition entered the Weddell Sea and was shortly crushed to splinters. The *Deutschland* of Professor Wilhelm Filchner's German expedition of 1911 nearly met a similar fate. In 1956 the vessel *Theron,* bringing supplies to a British base, was threatened but eventually managed to work free of the crushing complex of floes.

The cause of the danger lies in a clockwise circulation

of wind and water which jams the sea ice against the east coast of Palmer-Graham Land. A ship entering the western part of the Weddell Sea is soon in the position of a mite caught between the jaws of a colossal grist mill. The only feasible route of access to the coast is from the east along the coast of Queen Maud Land. But this was unknown to Shackleton, who entered boldly from the north and was quickly caught and held a prisoner of the drifting ice.

Shackleton always looked optimistically toward release ("soon, boys"), but the ice was unrelenting, and after a year of helpless drifting the *Endurance* was crushed. The wreckage sank beneath the ice and vanished. A complete catastrophe was avoided because much material was saved from the ship, including food, clothing, and three ship's boats. A camp was set up on the ice, which continued to drift to the northward. The movement of the floes was a constant hazard.

One night the ice parted directly beneath one of the tents, casting a man into the sea. Shackleton was nearby and quickly yanked the unfortunate fellow from the icy water. But in the confusion, the floe on which Shackleton stood drifted away into the darkness. Frank Wild, second in command, quickly launched one of the boats and brought his leader back to safety. It all happened so swiftly few thought of the danger. The night was cold and blowy, the air thick with snow. Had anyone *taken* the time to think, the story might well have had another ending.

As the drift continued, the ice became rotten; the survivors were forced to take to their boats, struggling hard to fend off sharp ice that threatened to puncture the eggshell sides, hauling them out to drag and manhandle them across broad wet floes, launching them again

and again into black ice-filled leads, struggling and straining until hearts nearly burst and minds secretly wondered
if escape from this gray semi-frozen chaos were possible.

But escape was possible. On April 14, 1916, after fourteen months (since February, 1915) at the mercy of the
terrible Weddell Sea, the expedition landed on Elephant
Island, an outpost of the South Shetlands. On reaching
the beach, the men were overcome with joy, "laughing
uproariously, picking up stones and letting handfuls of
pebbles trickle between their fingers like misers gloating
over hoarded gold." Shackleton too was gratified that land
was reached, but he now faced greater obstacles and
dangers than those recently overcome.

Elephant Island was uninhabited and lay outside the
regular whaling traffic. With winter approaching there
was not the slightest possibility of rescue by a passing
vessel. The nearest habitations were the British settle-
ments in the Falkland Islands to the north, and the
Norwegian whaling stations on South Georgia, eight hundred miles to the northeast. Somehow Shackleton must get
to one of these islands.

As two of the saved boats were too small and unseaworthy, all twenty-eight expedition members could not escape by this means. But the third boat, named *James Caird*
after the expedition's chief backer, was large and stronger,
and in her an ocean voyage did not seem an unreasonable
risk. In this vessel Shackleton resolved to make such a voyage, to sail with a small crew to some inhabited shore and
bring back a rescue ship for the remainder of his men.

The decision placed awful responsibilities on him. If he
did not get through, his men would perish without re-
course, or even knowledge of his fate. If he succeeded in
the boat voyage but was unable to return with help in
time, his conscience would carry an unspeakable burden.

For Shackleton to stay behind with his men, and die with them if that should become inevitable, was equally impossible, for his character demanded his own personal involvement and responsibility. His best reason for going, Frank Wild has told us, is that his men truly believed that Shackleton was the only one among them capable of making the dangerous voyage.

Bits and pieces saved from the *Endurance* were used to increase the seaworthiness of the twenty-three-foot vessel. Her sides were raised a precious few inches and her top was covered over with an improvised canvas deck to keep the water out. Her mast was stepped and fitted with a sail. The necessary gear and a small stock of provisions were placed on board. In late April, after a round of poignant farewells, Shackleton and a crew of five set sail. His course was laid for South Georgia. This meant sailing several hundred miles farther than to the Falklands, but in so doing he would be able to make use of the unrelenting westerlies, rather than oppose them.

There have been many small-boat voyages, both before and after Shackleton. Captain Bligh sailed 4000 miles from the mutinied *Bounty* to the island of Timor; Joshua Slocum went around the world in the *Spray;* and lately housewives have taken to crossing the Atlantic. But all these are fair-weather cruises compared with the voyage the *James Caird* made in the misty gray of antarctic winter across the wildest water in the world.

From the start, the voyage became two mortal struggles, one to keep the boat afloat and on course in mountainous seas, the other to preserve warmth and life in the bodies of her crew. The enemy always was the terrible weather in this No Man's Water where winds sweep unopposed around the globe. It is not cold as measured by the thermometer, but the atmosphere is raw, filled with moisture, rain, wet snow, salt spray, all whipped into a frenzy. It is the weather of Kamchatka and the Aleutians, of the Faeros and the North Sea in winter, all rolled in one but twice as bad.

One moment the *James Caird* lay in the hollow between great waves, her sail slack in an eerie calm; the next she careened wildly to the top of a snarling crest, exposed to the full strength of the gale. She took water with every sea. Without her frail canvas deck she would have been swamped within the first hour; with it, she nevertheless had to be bailed out constantly. While two of her crew struggled with this, a third sat bent to the

The launching of the *James Caird*, Elephant Island, 1916. In this small vessel Shackleton made the stormy, 800-mile voyage to South Georgia.

tiller, and the remaining three lay damp and cold in un-
refreshing sleep.

Occasionally Frank Worsley, skipper of the *Endurance*
who came along as navigator, got a glimpse of the sun
with his sextant; but for these glimpses, the *James Caird*
would never have found her way. Occasionally one or
another of the crew could creep forward to a tiny dry
space in the very bow and warm a pan of milk over a
small kerosene stove; or big Tom Crean, a venerable
veteran of three antarctic expeditions, would, amid wind
and sleet that chilled to the marrow, break into un-
melodious song. But for these small bits of cheer, gloom
would have turned to despair and worse. And always
indefatigable Shackleton, though racked with the pain of
sciatica, maintained good spirits and held out hope, say-
ing, "We'll make it, boys. Don't worry, we'll make it."

On the eleventh day the usual gale blew out of the
southwest, rolling the *James Caird* unmercifully, drench-
ing her with blasts of freezing spray. Yet Shackleton saw
cause for cheer. On the horizon was a thin white band of
clear sky. The band seemed to approach with unnatural
speed, and as he watched he realized the supreme moment
had come. The white streak was not a break in the overcast. It was the foaming crest of an immense wave. There
was time for one agonized shout. "For God's sake, hold
on!" And then the wall of water was on them. Thunder-
ing like a dozen Niagaras, it hurtled down on the *James
Caird,* rolling her until her keel showed, burying her
bow deep in raging green water, pouring tons of cold sea
down upon her.

Within thirty seconds the titanic wave had approached,
worked its terror, and passed. In its wake the *Caird* hung
sickeningly, a doomed vessel preparing to sink. But from
Shackleton came a second shout, and all hands fell to

bailing as they had never bailed before, frantically, with tin cups, hats, and bare hands. The fear of death in lonely seas flitted through each man's mind. In five minutes the boat's awful sluggishness was gone, and in ten she showed life once more. "During twenty-six years' experience of the ocean in all its moods I had not encountered a wave so gigantic. It was a mighty upheaval of the ocean, a thing quite apart from the big white-capped seas that had been our tireless enemies for many days."

Thus one day out of sixteen, one trial out of many. On May 8th the mountains of South Georgia hove into view. Two days later, after a furious buffeting in a ninety-mile-an-hour hurricane, a landing was made. Here was fresh water (for thirst had plagued half the voyage) and soft grass on which to lay sorely bruised and weary bones. Young albatross, helpless on the nest, provided welcome nourishment. It was a second deliverance, and Shackleton thanked Providence.

The *James Caird* had landed on the west coast of the island. Husvik and Stromness, the Norwegian whaling stations, were on the east coast, a hundred miles away and around the island by water. So weakened were three of the crew, so certain was Shackleton that the *James Caird* could not survive a second dangerous voyage, he determined to make the twenty-five-mile overland journey. The interior of South Georgia is a hogback of mountains, festooned with ice and snow, as beautiful as the Alps but wilder and grander, reflecting nature in a more violent mood. In Shackleton's time it was an unknown country not yet seen or traveled by men. His crossing was to be the first.

The three sick men were left behind at King Haakon Bay where the *Caird* had landed. The others, Worsley, Crean, and Shackleton, set out on the last desperate leg

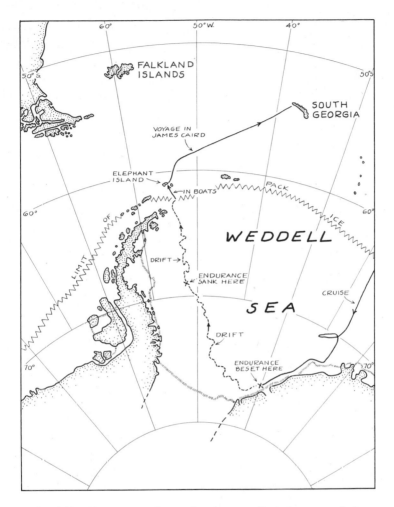

Shackleton's escape from the ice, ending in one of the most daring small-boat voyages in modern history.

of their mission. There was not a whole suit of clothes among them, no tent, no sleeping bag, and, except for a length of ship's rope, no alpine equipment. The tattered band scaled ridges, waded through snowfields, traversed glaciers. In the middle of the night, threatened with entrapment at high altitude by a fast-closing fog, they *slid* down a nine-hundred-foot snow slope, not knowing what lay below, only hoping they would land in one piece. The next morning they stumbled into the whaling station at Husvik, a frightening sight and unrecognizable to the station manager, who had bid them farewell when the expedition set out two years before.

Such were the outward effects of the ordeal, which soap and warm water, food and rest soon set right. But the inward effects were another matter, especially to Shackleton, who bore more than the rest. "We had suffered, starved and triumphed, groveled down yet grasped at glory, grown bigger in the bigness of the whole. We had seen God in His splendors, heard the text that Nature renders. We had reached the naked soul of man."

Shackleton now organized the relief of the Elephant Island party. After three heartbreaking failures in various ships which were stopped by ice, the Chilean steamer *Yelcho* made good. All the men who had been left behind were alive and happy, though weak from short rations and raw weather. In subsequent months the story of another failure unfolded. The *Aurora* had landed her party successfully, but in laying depots for Shackleton's transcontinental party, three men perished. The ship suffered ice damage to her rudder, which put her in great danger during her return to Australia for the first winter. Shackleton personally joined in the relief efforts which resulted in the withdrawal from Antarctica of the last remnants of his disastrous expedition.

Heartsore and tired, physically weakened after twenty years of toil in search of adventure and geographical prizes, Shackleton needed rest. But his mind brimmed with ideas and grand plans. His unquenchable enthusiasm for struggle would not let him rest. In 1922, forty-seven years old, Shackleton rose to the antarctic challenge once more; a new expedition was mounted. It could have been his best work. It was abruptly his last.

The ship *Quest* was procured, a leaky unseaworthy tub whose engines wheezed. The plan was to circumnavigate the continent in her, making a grand tour of unsounded seas, charting unfamiliar coasts, dredging the depths and sampling the atmosphere. She anchored at South Georgia for repairs after the long run south. Shackleton, a poet beneath the rugged exterior, wrote in his journal one night: "In the darkening twilight I saw a lone star hover, gemlike above the bay." These peaceful words were his last. Several hours later he was dead of heart failure.

Faithful Frank Wild finished the work begun, and good results were rung up by the expedition. But without Shackleton some vital element was missing, and all the party's efforts seemed anticlimactic. The great man had passed and everything seemed a little less worth doing. His death, indeed, marked the end of an era. After Shackleton, antarctic exploration became less and less a matter of men and muscle facing unknown hazard, and more and more men and machines facing calculated risk. But no one forgets the indomitable Shackleton. His life and struggles are an inspiration; his grave on lonely South Georgia is a monument to antarctic trial and tribulation.

8

Whale Oil and Maps

THERE HAD BEEN heroic strugggles and important discoveries, but great white spaces remained on the map of Antarctica. Even the coastline, the most accessible part of the continent, was a broken chain. A butter shortage in Europe after World War I did much to mend the chain and color the map.

The connection between these apparently unconnected ideas was provided by oleomargarine and whales. Advances in food chemistry made it possible to convert the rich but evil-smelling oil rendered from the tissues of a whale into a white fat widely acceptable as a substitute for butter. And the whale-oil whales, once scattered in every ocean of the globe, are now concentrated in the deep-water fringe around Antarctica.

In 1860 the Norwegian Svend Foyn invented the harpoon gun and explosive harpoon. Although forty years passed before these devices were perfected and reached widespread use, the event marked the beginning of modern antarctic whaling. Foyn's invention not only eliminated the dangers of old-time hand harpooning, but it made kills quicker and more certain. Mounted in the bow of a fast steam-driven "catcher" boat—also a Norwegian invention—the harpoon gun made it possible to run down the huge, swift blue and fin whales which abound in the antarctic, a feat undreamed of in the days of wooden whaleboats.

At the end of the last century Captain Carl A. Larsen of Norway sailed to the antarctic with the new weapons, one of the first skippers to do so. While in the Weddell Sea looking for whales, he discovered a stretch of the mountainous east coast of Palmer-Graham Land. It appropriately bears the name Svend Foyn Coast on modern maps. Acting on his estimate of the great whale-hunting potential of the untapped southern seas, Larsen established a permanent shore base for his company on South Georgia, calling it Grytviken. Other whalers followed, the Scottish and British establishing themselves at Leith, more Norwegians at Husvik and Stromness. The whaling stations on South Georgia, the closest approach to antarctic towns, became the center of a growing industry. The catch increased from almost nothing in 1900 to 40,000 whales in the 1930-31 season.

This prodigious growth resulted in part from the development in the 1920's of a third major improvement in the technique of whaling. This was the open-ended factory ship (see below) which made it possible to kill, butcher, and process whales on the high seas without coming near shore stations for weeks or months at a time. Loosed from their tethers, the whalers were now free to wander where they pleased in search of oil. Few wandered farther or with more fruitful results than Lars Christensen.

Christensen was not a captain but an owner. His father had financed Larsen's operations, and the family name runs through the history of antarctic whaling like a bright thread in a heavy shawl. Lars' hobby was exploration, but not from the armchair. Beginning in 1926, he yearly ordered at least one ship of his fleet to engage in exploring activities, partly to discover the migration habits of whales on which his industry depended, and partly just to discover.

In 1929 he equipped his exploring ship *Norvegia* with

a seaplane. His pilot was Hjalmar Riiser-Larsen, an experienced arctic flyer who was among the earliest to fly in the antarctic. The new machine quickly proved to be the explorer's most powerful tool (see Chapter 10). Taking off from open water at the edge of the pack in the region south of Africa, Riiser-Larsen quickly flew over tangled, grinding floes that no ship could have penetrated alive.

Beyond loomed the elusive coast, unseen since the English sealing captain John Biscoe had sighted a fragment of it a hundred years before. Riiser-Larsen made repeated flights, the ship gradually working eastward, and by season's end more than 1,300 miles of new coastline were added to the charts. The land that lay behind the coast was called Queen Maud Land and claimed for Norway. The next year the region was visited again to fill in the gaps in the immense discovery, the most extensive since Ross and Wilkes sailed a century before.

Curiosity now drew Christensen to the east. As each season passed he became more interested in exploration, perhaps less in whaling. No longer content to send others, he personally boarded his exploring plane for flights over the white regions. To show how tame this brand of exploration was, he was frequently accompanied by his wife. (Although Christensen well knew that the risks were there, ready to confound the careless or foolhardy.) In 1937 the sounding apparatus of his ship revealed a rise in the ocean floor. He named it Four Ladies Bank after his wife, daughter, and two women guests who had accompanied him!

Christensen's career in the antarctic spanned a fruitful decade. Either he or his captains made discoveries that linked Wilkes Land with Palmer-Graham Land and filled in over one quarter of the coastal perimeter of the continent. Geographers and other explorers have recognized their debt to this unique businessman-explorer, and his name is preserved in several places on the map of Antarctica. Ultimately of course it was the persistent and profitable pursuit of whales that made it all possible, for without whale oil to sell Christensen probably could not have afforded so costly a hobby.

Fabulous creatures, but dimly aware of what the world holds for them, the basis of the only antarctic industry, whales are quite as inseparable as penguins from the antarctic scene. Although they were once the object of mystery and fright, a hundred years of difficult study accompanied often with honest amazement have shed much light on them, and the whale tribe today is fairly well sorted out.

In primordial times the whale was a land mammal. Subsequently he took to the sea. When or for what purpose is unknown, but the new environment not only changed his way of life but his body as well. Fore limbs became swimming flippers; hind limbs disappeared altogether, and at the end of the spine there developed a broad propulsive tail. So streamlined and fish-like has the whale's body become, there is not the slightest external evidence of this unexpected origin. The whole story has been deduced from its skeleton.

The body hair characteristic of most mammals is absent from whales, except for a few whiskers or horny knobs around the lips of some species. Its place has been taken by a thick layer of oil-filled tissue, the "blubber" of the whalemen, which provides some insulation against the cold of the waters the whale inhabits. The rest of the whale's body is also somewhat oily, and even the bones have an oily matrix in the center. All of this is of utmost significance to the whaling industry, whose wish is that the whale might be all oil!

Whale babies are born alive at sea—something of a miracle, as zoologists are as yet uncertain how the new-born calf avoids drowning in the first few minutes of life. Feeding the calf is unusual because the whale's lips are stiff and immovable, but the job is accomplished by the tongue, which is curled into a tube-like shape. When the mother whale is nuzzled, she discharges a strong jet of milk directly into the tube. The milk, containing fifty per cent fat, is exceedingly rich when compared with cow's milk, which is four per cent fat.

Whales do not spout water, although the idea that they do is still widespread. Were a whale to draw water into its blowhole, which is in reality a nostril, it would promptly drown, as would any air-breathing animal that flooded its lungs. The spout is a plume of "steam" that condenses when the animal exhales the warm moist air stored in its lungs. It is exactly the same as the vapor which pours from human mouths on a cold day. In the antarctic the conditions are ideal for the formation of the feathery plume. Occasionally, if the whale begins to blow just before reaching the surface, there will be a small amount of water in the spout, but this comes from outside and is accidental.

The whale has prodigious breath-holding ability. It is thought that the sperm whale can stay below for an hour and a quarter as a matter of course. An enormous rib cage and great lung capacity are undoubtedly part of the explanation. But is all the air held in the lungs? In preparing for a dive a whale may make fifty or sixty "blows" on the surface, more than enough for a simple change of air in the lungs. Whale meat is the reddest known. The red color is caused by the hemoglobin of the blood, the chemical which absorbs oxygen and carries it to all body tissues. It is probable that the whale can store a significant

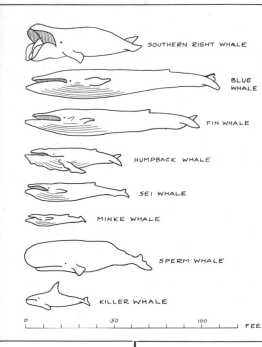

SOUTHERN RIGHT WHALE

BLUE WHALE

FIN WHALE

HUMPBACK WHALE

SEI WHALE

MINKE WHALE

SPERM WHALE

KILLER WHALE

0   50   100   FEET

A comparison of various whales encountered in the antarctic and (below) graphic illustration of how big a big blue whale really is. (After Machowski)

ONE LARGE BLUE WHALE IS THE EQUIVALENT OF

25 ELEPHANTS, OR

150 BULLS !

amount of oxygen in his blood vessels, much more propor-
tionately than other mammals, and draw on this reserve
supply while submerged.

Twelve species of whale frequent the antarctic. Fewer
than half are of interest to whalemen, but those that are
include some mighty specimens. The blue whale may
exceed one hundred feet in length and one hundred fifty
tons in weight. Appearing in older books as Sibbald's
rorqual or the sulfur-bottomed whale, the blue is the true
and original leviathan. It is considered by zoologists to
be the largest animal ever known to have existed.

Swimming at top speeds of over twelve knots, the muscles driving the tail and flukes of the average blue de-
velop 1,700 horsepower. In making comparisons, the blue
whale stands somewhere between a herd of twenty elephants and a railroad locomotive. But for all its great
size and strength, the whale's bones are disproportionately
thin for the weight of flesh clinging to them. The bigger
whales are quite incapable of supporting their own weight
out of water. The burden is borne by the buoyant force
of the water displaced in the manner of a ship or, more
accurately, a submarine. The fate of a whale stranded on
a beach is to die of broken ribs and crushed internal
organs.

Because of the large amount of oil that can be rendered
from a single carcass, the blue whale is the most valuable
to the whaling industry; but there are others which must
not be passed over. Similar to the blue, but smaller, is
the fin whale, which reaches a maximum length of about
eighty feet. Together with the blue, it constitutes the
major part of the antarctic catch. Smaller still and of
correspondingly less value are the sei whale and the minke
whale or lesser rorqual, neither of which attains a length
of even fifty feet.

All are members of a group known as the whalebone or baleen whales, characterized by the growth from the upper jaw of hundreds of fringed plates of this horny substance. These whales have no teeth, and the lower jaw is simply a receptacle for the baleen, which grows to great length in some species. Baleen is known chemically as keratin and is therefore the same material as that found in human fingernails. A strip of it is strong and flexible, and in another day was used for buggy whips and corset stays. The substance was then of such great value that in the arctic, especially, the oil was ignored and only the baleen taken. Growing in mass in the whale's mouth, it resembles the long close-set bristles of a huge brush. It serves the same purpose as a soup strainer.

A baleen whale feeds by cruising at the surface with its mouth ajar. Its principal food is "krill," a shrimp-like crustacean about three inches long which floats on the surface of antarctic waters in astronomical numbers. When the whale's mouth is full of krill and water, he presses his tongue upward, forcing out the water but not the

Euphausia superba, the shrimp-like organism which is the principal food of the antarctic baleen whales.

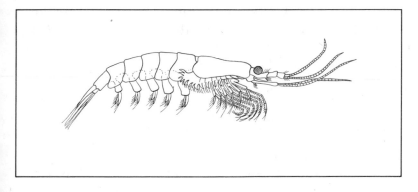

krill, which cannot pass through the dense fringe of baleen. An ingenious mechanism by which the largest of sea creatures feeds on one of the smallest!

The opening pages of *Moby Dick,* the most famous of all whaling books, contain a statement which reads: "In the year 1690 some persons were on a high hill observing the whales spouting and sporting with each other, when one observed: there—pointing to the sea—is a green pasture where our children's grandchildren will go for bread." We do not know how this suggestion was regarded then, but today, not quite three hundred years later, it is far from fanciful.

The baleen whales and the krill on which they feed are members of a food chain that has gained the attention of man, whose increasingly populous world has a Damoclean food shortage hanging over it. Animals cannot manufacture their own food and must ultimately depend on green plants, which accomplish this through the process of photosynthesis. Man's handicap is that he is running out of space for the growing of edible plants, not to mention space for the grazing animals which provide his favorite food, namely meat.

Krill, being themselves animals, must also feed on plants, the one-celled plant plankton found in the upper thirty feet or so of the cold ocean water that lies within the Antarctic Convergence. But the beauty of krill is that the plants on which it feeds are not only unpalatable to man but virtually inaccessible. Also, it converts the plant material into edible protein more efficiently than do sheep or cattle. It is not an accident that the whale in its evolution has sought out this small creature; no other so readily supplies the enormous quantities of rich food required, which for a growing blue whale may be three tons per day.

Since the red *Euphausia superba,* which is the principal

member of the vast krill population, not only looks like a shrimp but also tastes like one, man may choose to make direct use of this inhabitant of Neptune's pasture. If his craving for meat persists, he may ascend the food chain one link and eat whale's flesh, as is presently done in Japan and Norway, where it is favorably compared with beef if prepared with the necessary art. Or he may easily contrive a use for the phenomenally rich whale's milk— although the technique of milking whale cows has not yet been developed.

But these exotic uses of the resources of the antarctic lie largely in the future. Present whaling activities are preeminently concerned with whale oil, which when treated with hydrogen gas in the presence of certain catalysts becomes oleomargarine. In this form the ocean pastures are truly providing an adjunct to man's bread, if not yet the bread itself.

The key men in the hunt for oil are the harpooners. On their aim and hunting skill hangs the success or failure of a season in the south. The Svend Foyn harpoon gun has been mentioned. In practice it consists of a heavy muzzle-loading barrel mounted on a swivel. The charge is black powder, a wooden wad, and the iron shank of a two-hundred-pound harpoon. The whole apparatus is mounted on a platform in the bow of a catcher.

This vessel is the outsized descendant of the wooden whaleboat. Varying in length from one hundred to one hundred fifty feet, the catcher is narrow in the beam for fast maneuvering. Her forefoot is much cut away, and the bows have a wide flare to protect the harpooner from water. With a powerful engine, the sleek ship is sometimes a danger to herself.

In 1947 the English catcher *Simbra* was twenty miles from her factory ship, chasing a whale downwind in an ice-free sea. She was low on fuel and high in the water. A sudden hard turn caused her to lean over too far. She fell on her side and sank within fifteen minutes. Sixteen men managed to get into a lifeboat, but their clothing was wet through, and the cold air lay like a killing blanket on the ocean. When help came, fifteen hours later, only one man remained alive.

On the catcher's mast is a crow's nest, and from here rings out the anxiously awaited cry of *"Hvalblast!"* (Though the ship be English, half her crew will be Norwegian.) The harpooner, usually the captain, dashes to the gun platform along a catwalk leading from the bridge. The mate is ready at the wheel, the engineer below. There is no suggestion of a stalk. The engines are

A modern whale catcher. The harpooner's platform and catwalk to the bridge may be seen.

Hector Whaling Co.

wide open and their throbbing is audible under the sea for miles around.

The whale breaks the surface in graceful arcs. The curving back, exposed for perhaps thirty seconds at a time, is the harpooner's target. Subtle movements of hands and arms direct the helm. Unexpectedly, for only the harpooner knows precisely the right moment, the gun lets go with a roar.

The harpoon line flies out in a descending arc, first the foregoer of stranded nylon an inch and a quarter in diameter, then the back-up line of heavier manila. The harpoon strikes with a thud, scarcely felt by the whale. But three seconds later a fused charge in the harpoon head explodes, causing folded barbs to fly out and lodge the missile firmly in the tissues. This the whale very noticeably feels. Wild with pain, it reacts violently and unpredictably, combining the fury of a bull with the strength of a runaway freight train.

It may dive deep—sounding, the whalers call it—coming up a few minutes later, a spectacle of blood, foam and anger. Or the whale brain may decide upon a run for it on the surface. Whatever the reaction, the early seconds after a hit are full of danger and excitement for the whalemen, especially the harpooner, who wisely beats a retreat from his exposed position. The whale line runs out at a furious pace, ready to slice in two the fool who gets caught in its flying coils.

The bitter end is fastened to the drum of a powerful winch on deck. In some catchers the line is threaded through strong blocks to the top of the mast, which acts as a huge fishing rod, its springiness preventing the line from being snapped by a sudden strain. If the whale slacks off slightly, the winch reels in line. If it swims, the catcher follows. If the opportunity arises the harpooner

will take a second and a third shot with explosive har-
poons. It is a grand, frightful, pathetic, unequal struggle, a
monster of flesh and bone pitted against a monster of
steel with bombs and cables and grinding engines to do
its work. Few whales survive more than an hour of battle.

The carcass is brought alongside and pumped full of
air to prevent its sinking. The broad tail flukes are cut off
to facilitate handling at the factory ship. The lifeless
hulk is marked with a red flag—and lately with a small
automatic radio transmitter—so that it can be found later
for towing to the ship. The catcher cuts loose to search
for more oil.

Somewhere within a radius of a hundred miles is the
factory ship, part mechanical monster, part mother bird
anxious over her brood of darting catchers. The factory
ship is a Brobdingnagian butcher's shop, an oil cookery,
a tanker, a fertilizer plant, and a floating apartment house
for the hundreds of workers who live aboard and operate
her. The whalemen insist she is the ugliest vessel afloat.

Her two funnels are not in line but side by side, an
arrangement made necessary by the position of the boilers
below, but one which completely destroys any resemblance to a normal ship. At the stern is a gaping hole
which reaches to the water line and is large enough to
admit a railway car. This gives the appearance of a landing craft turned around, but the factory ship is fifty times
bigger. From the opening a steel skidway rises gently to
the main deck, a vast arena whose fore and aft sections
can easily accommodate four ninety-ton whales in various
stages of dismemberment.

Whales are brought to the stern opening tail first. The
ten-ton *hval kla*—another Norwegian invention that resembles a giant ice tongs—settles on the stumps of the
flukes, and a powerful winch smoothly draws the animal

The ribs are torn loose from a blue whale, a mighty "side o' bacon," a single rib of which dwarfs a man.

C. E. Ash

up to the after deck. Here men called flensers perform
an ancient task, cutting off the blubber in thick strips.
Their tools are strange-looking knives, shaped like hockey
sticks and razor sharp on both edges, a design that has
barely changed in a hundred years. Deftly, swiftly, the
blubber is cut into convenient chunks. Nimble "blubber
boys" drag it to manholes which lead to the factory below,
where steam cookers render out the precious oil, which is
run into tanks for the long voyage home.

In the days of hand whaling, only the blubber was
taken, as there was no way to handle the enormous hulk
that remained. On the modern factory ship flensing is
only the beginning. The lemmers take over now, their
job being to cut off the oil-bearing meat in great red gobs
and send it below to another set of cookers. This done,
the carcass is hauled to the forward deck, where steam-
powered saws are used to dismember it still further, and
the sawed-up bones are sent to still another set of cookers.
Little of the whale is wasted. The residue from the cookers
is reduced to a dry powder used for fertilizer. The skull
is opened and the five-ounce pituitary gland which rests
on the top of the brain is removed for the drug industry.
The liver, which weighs nearly a ton, is processed for
the chemicals it contains. What is left, the stomach and
intestines, is tossed over the side.

If catching whales is dangerous, cutting them up is
more so. The decks of the factory ship are a no man's land,
slippery with blood and oil, where a maze of straining
steel cables, swinging blocks, and ten-ton whale parts can
easily deal death to the unwary.

But danger is a characteristic of the whole whaling
industry, a strange enterprise, half sport, half noxious
labor, cruel on one hand, fascinating on the other, and all
of it taking place on the stormy lonely fringe of Antarc-

Blubber is cut off in strips and then sent to cookers below.

C. E. Ash

tica. And the men who go a-whaling are a breed apart, not content with smoky streets and neon signs, gladly exchanging these for the crystal air of the antarctic world, which clears the head and whets the appetite.

The only question remaining concerns the whales themselves. Can they survive the relentless hunting? The humpback whale is virtually extinct, though once it was a favorite. The big blues, over ninety feet long, are rarely seen. And the demand is for more and more whales. As the world population grows the hunger for fats and oils becomes increasingly insatiable. In 1958-59 the total antarctic whale catch was 36,196—a loss which biologists say the slow-breeding leviathans cannot endure for very long without disastrous effects. Of this number only 1,191 were blue whales, a warning that the big whales are already extremely scarce.

Theoretically whaling is under the control of an international commission which sets limits on the numbers and sizes of whales that can be taken. But the regulations are difficult to enforce, and some nations show a frank unwillingness to abide by the rules, preferring to grab what they can while they can. One fine day the whaling industry may suddenly be all over.

9

Men Among the Penguins

WHEN THE FRENCH explorer Jean Rivolier returned from the antarctic he lamented, "I have often tried to tell my friends about the experiences we had . . . but from their questions it has always emerged that they were much more interested in the (penguins) than in ourselves."

This plight is inevitable. We all know what penguins look like, having seen them in pictures, or movies, or if fortunate in a zoo. But the penguin is not communicative, and at times he is mystical, a circumstance that has bred unsatiable curiosity in man.

An obvious explanation is the man-like appearance of the penguin—white "shirt," black "coat," erect posture, and shuffling gait. What we see before us is not a strange animal from the south but a ridiculous miniature caricature of ourselves whose comical antics never grow tiresome—for man never tires of watching himself—and whose resemblance is close enough to be amusing but not so close as to be embarrassing. But there is a serious side to the matter and the penguin represents a genuine antarctic problem, all of whose aspects have not yet been solved.

Seventeen species of penguins are recognized in the southern hemisphere, but many of these inhabit such unlikely places as Africa, New Zealand, and South America, where they bask in cold currents. Most are relegated to the sub-antarctic islands such as South Georgia and Macquarie, the latter famous for its vast rookeries. Only four species habitually reach the shores of the antarctic continent. These are polar veterans with twice the fascination of their less adventuresome cousins.

Of these, two stand out as the archetypes of the penguin world: the Adelie penguin and the Emperor penguin. Yet except for general coloring, two related creatures could hardly be less alike. The Adelie, named for the wife of the early explorer Dumont D'Urville, is small (two feet tall) and light (six to fourteen pounds), wears a preposterous white ring around each eye, and is irresistibly amusing. The Emperor is tall (four feet) and heavy (up to ninety pounds), wields a vicious beak, and can break a man's arm with a sharp blow of its wing. Both have held the close attention of scientists for at least fifty years, and have shed much light on the affairs of the whole family.

Penguins are birds. They possess many undoubted bird characteristics, particularly an outer covering of feathers. But they are unlike any other birds in the world. Not only do they not fly, but unlike other flightless birds, their wings provide little evidence that they have ever known how to fly. Indeed, some zoologists prefer to call these structures flippers rather than wings. The penguin is an aquatic bird and spends most of its time in the water. Its three-toed feet are webbed, but it uses them little if at all in swimming, propelling itself through the water with its wings instead.

Except for the auk family of the northern hemisphere, no other swimming birds use their wings in the water, and these do not approach the penguin in efficiency and grace. The swimming motion is such that it may be quite accurately said that the penguin "flies" through the water. The underwater flight is powerful and swift, some birds being clocked at up to twenty-two miles per hour.

A favorite way of leaving the water is to swim full speed toward the surface, like a black-and-white subaqueous missile, and in one continuous motion shoot through the air and land feet first on ice or rocks. The Emperor is capable of getting to the top of a five-foot ledge in this manner, and this constitutes its nearest and only approach to flight.

It is known that birds have evolved from reptiles, specifically from the dinosaurs that once roamed the earth in great numbers and varieties. The story cannot be detailed here, but the fossil clues are abundant. The reconstructed *Iguanodon,* for example, is a dinosaur bearing an undeniable resemblance to a gigantic plucked chicken. *Archaeopteryx,* on the other hand, is an extinct flying form so reptile-like in general structure that only the presence of fossilized feathers affirms its status as a true bird. Feathers are, in fact, the hallmark of birds, and a study of their evolution shows them to be a complex development of reptilian scales. In this theoretical picture the penguin has a place, but it is by no means definitely established.

Two possibilities appear to exist. The penguin may represent an arrested stage in bird evolution. Thus, while other birds gradually developed the power of flight, the penguin for some undetermined reason has never progressed beyond its present state. It has obviously come a long way down the path of bird development already, but it is an interesting speculation and, if verified, the penguin will stand as a living "missing link" between modern birds and their flightless ancestors.

The other possibility is that the penguin once could fly and has for some again undetermined reason lost the ability. If the probabilities here are higher, the explanation is no less difficult, for the heavy body and small wings indicate that flight was abandoned far back in its history. The penguin shows not even the dimmest instinct for flight and never flaps its wings in the manner of other flightless birds—although it possesses the common bird characteristic of tucking its head under its wing when sleeping. The problem is now further complicated by the discovery in New Zealand and elsewhere of jumbo fossil penguins estimated to have stood five feet high and weighed two hundred pounds.

Antarctica is not incidental to the story, having discouraged all other major forms of life, which found its environment too harsh. But the penguin flocks to its shores in galactic numbers each summer. The exception is the Emperor penguin, which sticks it out in the antarctic all year round. No more profound example of stark survival in the face of extreme odds can be found than the life of the Emperor.

It is true that the krill upon which penguins largely feed, the same pink crustacean that nourishes the big whales, is confined to the antarctic regions. But penguins are not the specialized feeders that whales are, and in captivity they have survived on a variety of sea life, including fish. Why then are they confined to the antarctic?

One theory is that the penguins have been driven south by the more adaptable and hence more successful warm-climate forms, against whom they fought an ever-losing battle for available food. Another is that the penguin is an antarctic aborigine whose origin in the far south predates the present cold climate. When the climate changed, the penguin alone, by this theory, was sufficiently adaptable to survive, while all other forms either perished or migrated to warmer regions. Thus we have the penguin cast in one of two quite different roles.

To unravel some of the perplexities, man has had to go among the penguins. The French expedition of which Jean Rivolier was a member spent a year at Point Geologie in Adelie Land, where one of the few known Emperor penguin rookeries is located. Leader Mario Marret stated that the main purpose of the expedition was "to study the whole annual cycle of their lives, making films and sound recordings." This was the first time a whole expedition had devoted itself to penguins; the results were necessarily exceptional.

A hut was built at the edge of the rookery and installed with human observers, who took turns observing every penguin move. The fortunes of the living and the as yet unborn were pursued with equal vigor. Eggs were regularly borrowed from brooding birds. Chicks were hatched in captivity. A few poor grown birds were sacrificed on the dissecting table. And throughout the year a respectable number found their way into the cooking pots, for roast penguin breast is a fishy-tasting but not unacceptable food.

It is not correct to say that the Emperor spends *all* his time in Antarctica. The summer months of January and February are spent at sea, feeding up on krill in preparation for the winter. Just where is unknown, for no one has succeeded in tracing the Emperor to his summer haunts. Then, early in March, when all other birds have gone north after a brief summer in the south, the stolid Emperor makes his appearance. First in twos and threes, then in dozens, finally in hundreds, leaping out of the water, preening themselves, and waddling off with dim purposiveness toward the rookery.

The rookery is nothing more than a communal nesting place. It has no special characteristics, for the Emperor chooses to nest not on shore but on the sea ice nearby. It is doubtful whether the word nest should even be used, for the ice provides no materials and the Emperor builds no nest. His harsh lot is clear from the outset, for he is deprived even at birth of what is certainly a fundamental institution of birddom: the warmth, coziness, and security of a fixed home.

The Emperor is unperturbed. If the ice is weak and breaks up in a blow, he stoically wins through to firmer stuff, though some of his brothers may have perished in the cataclysm. By the end of April, 1952, the year of observation at Point Geologie, the ice was firm, the rookery extended many acres and numbered ten thousand birds —a large population by antarctic standards. Two unmistakable characteristics of a large rookery were present: a constant raucous din of squawking birds and a horrendous stench.

The purpose of the coming ashore is to lay eggs, but this can occur only after mating has taken place. It is a process that is comical and pathetic, for the birds are inordinately stupid (aiding or belying their resemblance

Emperor penguins.

Official U.S. Navy Photo

to man?). To the layman there is no observable difference in the appearance of the sexes. Males look exactly like females, and vice versa. Even the experts can never be certain.

This includes the penguins themselves, for male birds are often seen courting birds which, alas, ultimately prove to be males too. Or maybe they were both females! There is much petty bickering and fighting, for each hen (if we may use the term) has her bevy of suitors who vie for her attention. Often enough she wanders off unconcernedly in the middle of it all and the victor finds he has fought over nothing. But in the end a degree of tranquillity prevails, and the paired birds await the egg.

This treasured, more-priceless-than-gold object makes its appearance some time during the month of May. It is the shape of a chicken's egg, but larger, five inches long and one pound in weight. To keep it off the ice, it is skillfully held on the top of the feet. To keep it warm, it is pressed against a convenient patch of bare skin on the underside of the hen's breast. Despite reverential respect for the egg, accompanied by much irreverent crowing, the penguin's unintelligence and clumsiness lead him to disastrous mistakes.

Fumbling with the egg may cause it to roll to the ice. If the tiniest crack appears, no chick will be born. If some petty interruption causes the egg to become chilled for a short time, no chick will appear. If, as often happens, marauding skua gulls are on hand, a momentarily abandoned egg will be snatched outright from the defenseless parents. In penguin land, above all, it is wise not to count chicks before they are hatched.

In the winter of 1911 a party from Scott's base on Ross Island journeyed to the then newly discovered rookery at Cape Crozier to procure Emperor eggs for study. Winter is not a good time for travel in the antarctic, especially in the early days, and this particular journey has come down in polar history as the worst in the world. The three men in the party, Edward Wilson, H. R. Bowers, and Apsley Cherry-Garrard, came very close to not getting out alive. Their ordeal was not merely to survive in a tent in temperatures of 76° below zero, but to travel by arduous and inefficient manhauling.

"The horror of the nineteen days it took us . . . would have to be re-experienced to be appreciated. . . ." All the hardship was doubled because of the darkness, and defective trail techniques caused sleeping bags and clothing to freeze to the consistency of armor plate. The simple acts of living, eating, sleeping, moving, were compound agonies. Cherry-Garrard's fingers were lost in a large mass of frostbite blisters. The water in these froze to ice and his hands became painful monstrosities resembling deformed bunches of petrified grapes. Nonetheless the rookery was reached and the party returned with three eggs for science carefully carried in woolen socks and mittens hung about their necks. But ". . . anyone would be a fool who went again. . . ."

The great value of the eggs was the opportunity they would afford for the study of the penguin embryo—the as yet unborn chick. It is a principle of biology that the development of the embryo closely parallels in some respects the development of the species over thousands of years, that every organism in the embryonic state goes through the same evolution from simplicity to complexity as life itself has gone through during its history on earth.

Hope was particularly held that the embryos of these primitive birds would show in a decisive way the development of bird feathers from reptile scales. Unfortunately the results of this first venture of men among the penguins were inconclusive, although the primitiveness of the bird was again confirmed. The overriding pity was that after surviving this worst journey, two of the men, Wilson and Bowers, perished on Scott's ill-fated polar trek the following summer.

The French expedition at Point Geologie was able to conduct egg studies under less distressing circumstances. There were the warm hut, X-ray equipment for examining the contents of an egg undisturbed, and thermocouple devices for determining incubation temperatures. And there was Arthur, an endearing penguin chick hatched out in captivity and for a time destined to be the first Emperor penguin raised by man.

But Arthur's sleeping place, for purposes of warmth, was in the oven. And one night the wind rose, the fire roared, and upon opening the oven door the next morning poor Arthur was found "done to a turn." He was soon followed by Arthur II, whom the biologist indulged supremely. To make his diet as normal as possible, his food was obtained by dissecting an adult penguin and extracting the contents of its stomach. This mass was entirely satisfactory to Arthur II, but it filled the hut with a noisome smell. Subsequently Arthur II and another chick developed into healthy adults.

At the rookery, matters are not always so scientifically pursued. At the time the egg is laid the adult birds have been without a scrap of food for two months or more, a challenging circumstance just before the onset of winter. Food must be had, and because of efforts already put forth the female is the first to get it. The egg is now passed to the male, who has the same means of warming it as the female, but considerably less skill. During the changeover and afterward, many more eggs are fumbled and cracked, or become frozen.

Eggs are rarely wilfully abandoned. Of all the penguins that have come ashore, only half have laid eggs. Should a single egg fall by the wayside, there is always an eggless bird on hand to assume responsibility for it. The brooding instinct is so strong that eggless birds will frequently seize upon a piece of ice and attempt to incubate it.

Among the Emperors, then, Father is responsible for the brooding. But Mother is not off on a holiday. The sea, once a few hundred yards away, is now widely frozen and the ice edge is sixty miles or more distant. It is a long journey for a hungry penguin, and there is always tragedy along the line. Members of the French party attempted to follow this winter migration of the females, but the ice was too dangerous in the poor light, the risks to human life too great. Thus there is another gap in our knowledge of the life cycle of this enigmatic bird.

Winter has now descended on the rookery and those brave birds staying on with the eggs face severe conditions. The marvelous down beneath their outer feathers is an efficient barrier against the cold. But the blizzard is a trial they cannot face alone. When a storm threatens—the penguins have an uncanny weather sense and always know ahead of time when it is going to blow—they slowly, clumsily (because of the eggs) move together to form a *testudo,* a living shield of tightly packed bodies.

It is roughly circular in shape, the outer birds standing with their backs outward, the inner birds with heads down and shoulders interlocked; nothing will move them until the blizzard dies. The heat generated in the interior of the living mass is often sufficient to melt the ice beneath them. At the worst times during the winter at Point Geologie, all six thousand wintering birds formed up into a single testudo.

During the severe winter month of July, approximately

sixty-three days after the eggs have been laid, the hatching out begins. In general shape the new chick resembles a species of pear. It is about six inches high (when it gains its shaky feet), is clothed in soft down of an all-over gray, and has broad white rings about its black eyes, which give it a comical owlish appearance. The father may have to preside at the hatching out. But more often than not the mother is back from her feeding expedition, sleek with newly acquired fat and with a stomach full of partially digested sea food which, upon regurgitation, is the "formula" for the new infant.

The males, now thin and ragged looking after as long as five months without food, leave the rookery at last and undertake an expedition of their own toward the sea. The chicks grow in size and strength and gradually begin their own unsteady explorations of the rookery. As their development proceeds, other adult birds may leave. The chicks are then gathered into a number of "nursery" groups tended by a few adult birds.

When a storm breaks, familiar tactics are resorted to; the chicks are herded together and protected by a ring of adult birds. Nevertheless, the casualties are high; single young birds caught outside the testudo by a storm have no chance of survival whatsoever. Rivolier reports that after a storm there may be fifty dead chicks at the Point Geologie rookery, and ". . . a hundred is nothing out of the ordinary." The elements, aided and abetted by skua gulls, who all winter seek out the weak and injured, exact a heavy toll. By spring only *one-quarter* of the number born will remain alive. Following the rules of natural selection, it is hoped that the survivors are strong and fit and capable of carrying these traits to the next generation.

In September the males are back in full strength, and in October spring has arrived. At the ice edge, which has once again moved closer to the rookery, there are now still newer arrivals, the young birds who were born the year before but did not accompany their parents on the return to the rookery in March. All winter they have been in the sea to the north, possibly close to the outer edge of the ice pack, where it is warmer. Exactly where is unknown; a further penguin mystery.

In early December molting of the chicks begins; they lose their gray down and assume coats almost indistinguishable from those of their parents. But they are still undersized and lacking in strength and there must be weeks of practice at swimming and fishing. This is a time of fun and play. Penguin companies and battalions march and drill on the ice. In the water there is darting and

Royal penguins crowd the beach on Macquarie Island.

A.N.A.R.E. Photo by Ivan Fox

diving for food, and frantic flights to escape the jaws of leopard seals and killer whales.

Alas, some few must perish, although the penguin is marvelously adept in the water, his primary element. On the ice much "tobogganing" is observed. This is an alternate mode of progression on the surface. The bird flops on its breast and propels itself forward by action of the wings and feet in a manner suggestive of a seal, but it is a swift motion and far more efficient in covering distance than the upright walk.

All individuals are now well-fed and getting stronger. The youngsters become expert swimmers and fishers. And at the end of the month, at a time when the men who have come among them are occupied with Christmas celebrations and the sea has melted to the old ice at the very edge of the rookery, the white-shirted horde takes its departure. They swim northward to their unknown summer grounds, where three months hence the yearly cycle of their lives will begin once more.

Not all antarctic penguins have the harsh lot of the Emperors. The Adelies, who also come to the continental shores, are not forced to face the winter months. The maturing and hatching of eggs and the rearing of the young is a much faster process, and the whole is accomplished within the summer months. Perhaps for this reason the Adelie is less reserved in its behavior than the phlegmatic Emperor. It is resentful of the intrusions of man, but once it is established that there is nothing to be done about it, the Adelie is curious and friendly. It is then that it becomes Antarctica's clown. The Adelie rookeries are located on ice-free land, and the bird has risen so high in the scale of penguin affairs that it builds a crude nest of pebbles.

To the north, on the sub-antarctic islands, is found the

King, a less rugged relative of the Emperor and a favorite
with zoos because of its ability to survive in warmer
climates. The Rockhopper and Macaroni penguins are
the dandies of the clan, sporting plumes and crests on
their heads. The Royal is a multitudinous species found
only on Macquarie Island, where it thrives in a raw
maritime climate. The Gentoo is the only penguin with
white on the top of its head. Sitting on a nest of tussock
grass among the crags of South Georgia, it is the most bird-
like of the unbird-like penguins—which are nevertheless
birds!

The fate of the penguins cannot be predicted. Population counts are difficult to make. More study of these
difficult-to-study birds is required. At one time the fat
on their breasts made them worthy prey of the oil hunters.
On the accessible islands thousands were slaughtered, and
extinction threatened some species. Now they are vari-
ously protected by the countries with antarctic interests.
On Macquarie Island, where the penguin population was
once down to seven hundred, the Royal rookery alone
covers sixty-five acres and houses over half a million birds.
But among the Emperors the French scientists saw evidence of a natural decline. Each year fewer return to the
rookeries. "The Antarctic," states Jean Rivolier, "always
has the upper hand."

10

Flying the Antarctic

THE RECURRING THEME in man's progress on earth is his
persistent study of the problems of a largely hostile environment and his persistent success in solving them and
bringing that environment under his control. In this
respect the history of man in the antarctic might be
viewed as a highly compressed history of man as an animal
on earth. In the incredibly short space of sixty years he has
risen from the status of a half-frozen grub crawling feebly
across the snow plain to a powerful winged master of
polar skies with no corner of the continent barred from
access. It is a creditable achievement; Nature herself
labored with the clumsy penguin for countless millennia
to gain antarctic flight, and failed.

The first antarctic flight was not a flight in the usual
sense but merely an ascent in a captive balloon—part of
the exploratory equipment brought south by Robert F.
Scott on his 1902 expedition. The maximum altitude
reached was eight hundred feet. From here the first antarctic aerial photograph was made, an interesting but un-
revealing view of the surface of the Ross Ice Shelf. The
ascent was little more than a novelty and hardly worth
the high cost of the equipment and the great effort required to transport the necessary hydrogen gas, highly
compressed in bulky steel cylinders.

But "firsts" are liable to this defect, and Scott's photographs were in fact the precedent for fantastic developments in exploration by aerial cameras; his choice of site
approached clairvoyance. To make the ascent he had

steamed into Balloon Inlet, an indentation in the eastern edge of the Ross Ice Shelf. This subsequently became the famous Bay of Whales and the center of one of the most extensive flying programs Antarctica has ever seen.

Airplane followed balloon, the first plane being in the hands of Sir Hubert Wilkins, who, in 1928, flew over Palmer-Graham Land and mistakenly concluded that it was an island rather than a peninsula. But this otherwise historic flight passed almost unnoticed, for there now bowed onto the scene a young naval officer of remarkable qualities. With the airplane as his weapon, he picked up the tatters of American antarctic ambition cast down by Wilkes three-quarters of a century before. He mounted five glorious expeditions, for three decades dominated the antarctic scene as no other man had done, and literally put America—he called it "Little America"—on the map of the southern hemisphere. His great tangible accomplishment was the exploration of some *two million* square miles of the earth's surface—a record which cannot be duplicated on this planet.

Richard Evelyn Byrd was better suited than most for a life of exploration. At the age of twelve "when most boys are content with games" he traveled around the world, an experience that at once set him apart and on his course. Then followed a brief career in the Navy and a thrice-broken leg which forced him to retire at the improbable age of twenty-seven.

During World War I he wormed his way back into service, became a Navy flier. Flying was still dangerous; engines were unreliable, the "crates" were flimsy. But Byrd thrilled to the work; he was ambitious, proud, and had "dreams that stormed in his mind like ocean gales. They were visions of conquest and exploration, an almost mystical impellent that drove him time and time again from one horizon to another." In 1925 the horizon lay north. He successfully planned and executed a flight from Spitsbergen to the north pole and back, in a few hours cutting a swath across the unknown, becoming the world's hero.

Three years later the horizon lay south. The major purpose of the new flight was "to explore and make an aerial survey of the lane of vision between our base and the south pole." Byrd also keenly hoped to become the first human being to hover over the earth's uttermost point in a flying machine.

To this end he injected a new quality into exploration: bigness. His equipment amounted to thousands of tons, his expenses to nearly a million dollars. The efforts of a generation before now seemed to be merely street singing outside the doors of Byrd's grand opera.

The essentials were two ships, three airplanes, a Ford snowmobile, prefabricated insulated panels for the construction of buildings, steel for three seventy-foot radio towers, Eskimo dogs, lightweight sledges (one a gift from Amundsen), skis, trail gear, fur clothing, windproofs, aviation gasoline (twenty-four tons), sewing machines, a complete machine shop, a library of technical and polar books, pins, matches, toothbrushes (thirty dozen), and a large box kite for investigating the state of the atmosphere hundreds of feet above the ground.

Little America, his base on the Bay of Whales, was not far from the site of Amundsen's *Framheim* of seventeen years before. But where the Norwegians had put up a single hut, Byrd's men constructed a small village, fifteen buildings and semi-buildings, and a score of kennels and caches, interconnected by a labyrinth of snow tunnels. It was not lavish. It was simply the largest, most expensive, most ambitious, most fully equipped, most efficient, most

audacious expedition that had ever taken to the antarctic field.

Preparations for the flight and other exploratory activities occupied the first winter and spring. A successful
depot-laying flight was made in November to the base of
the Horst which lay across Byrd's route midway between
Little America and the pole. Here were cached gasoline
and food stores to be picked up on the return leg of the
polar flight. The capacity and fuel consumption of Byrd's
polar plane, a big Ford tri-motor, were such that he could
not make the 1,500-mile flight nonstop. The total payload
was 15,000 pounds, every ounce carefully weighed and
deemed essential. Of this, six hundred pounds were comprised of Captain Ashley C. McKinley and his big mapping camera. So critical was the loading that without
McKinley a nonstop flight was possible; with him, impossible.

Keenly as Byrd burned for the adventure of the pole
itself, he could not come back empty handed. Indeed, he
could sacrifice neither, and therefore he would have both
—the pole *and* the pictures. This necessitated the added
risk of making several landings and take-offs on skis over
an unfamiliar snow surface, but "in the polar regions
there inevitably arise occasions when to succeed one must
take long chances."

A variety of special hazards face the antarctic flyer.
Engines are difficult ("agony") to start in extreme cold.
If adjustments and repairs are required, gloves get in the
way, yet bare fingers can scarcely cope with the cold
metal; flesh sticks, is frozen, torn. To start his engines,
Byrd covered them with canvas hoods, preheated them
with gasoline pressure stoves, poured in hot oil.

Only the best days are flying days. Despite this axiom,
sudden squalls can spring up and quickly wreck a plane.

Byrd lost one of his single-engine planes in this way; during a storm a 150-mile-an-hour gust picked up the craft from a frozen lake where it had landed and dashed it to pieces on the ice half a mile away.

The glare from snow and ice surfaces make landing more dangerous than usual. Unable to judge the nearness of the ground, a pilot may fly right into it, or, under-estimating the distance, he may try to land fifty feet up, with equally disastrous results. Byrd used smoke bombs to mark the surface and lessen these risks. Still, snow that appears smooth from five hundred feet may be rippled with hard frozen *sastrugi* that can shake a plane to pieces as soon as the skis touch down.

In flight all depends on the engines, reliable as care and ingenuity can make them, but not infallible. An un-seen flaw in a piece of metal, a speck of dirt in a car-

The *Floyd Bennett* at Little America. In the rear are two of the radio towers.

From *Little America* by Richard E. Byrd. Copyright 1930. Used by permission of G. P. Putnam's Sons

buretor jet—these could cause forced landings far from base. Anticipating this, Byrd included in his flight kit a complete trail outfit, sledges, tent, sleeping bags, and the rest. It was a dead weight that might never be touched— or might avert disaster.

Therefore it was not without some risk that on Thanksgiving Day, November 25, 1929, the meteorologist gave his final "now or never." The engines had been checked and tuned to the finest pitch. All the gasoline and gear had been weighed once more and stowed aboard. Captain McKinley and his big camera had taken a position between the windows in the waist. Byrd had deposited sealed instructions to be opened in the event of his failure to return. After all these things and hundreds more, including good-byes and handshakes, the big silvery duralumin monoplane, engines roaring, skis hissing, slid across the snow and then rose easily, even lightly, into the polar air.

The flight south was almost without incident. Good luck? "Victory," wrote Amundsen, "awaits him who has everything in order—luck, people call it. Defeat is certain for him who has neglected to take the necessary precautions in time; this is called bad luck." So with Byrd. His success was and would be based directly on his painstaking and exhaustive preparations.

One obstacle stood in Byrd's path: the Great Antarctic Horst, which holds back the flood of ice from the polar plateau. Some of its peaks approach heights of 15,000 feet. The tri-motor had insufficient power to fly over this mountain barrier, and Byrd's plan was to fly through it by way of one of the large glacier-filled passes that Amundsen had seen. But at the head of the Liv Glacier, at an altitude of 9,700 feet, the plane reached its ceiling and could climb no more. Ahead lay the top of the glacier and the edge of the plateau, at an altitude something in excess of 10,000 feet. A crisis was at hand. Bernt Balchen, the pilot, yelled that the plane must be lightened.

Byrd faced a crucial decision. If he jettisoned gasoline, the flight to the pole was finished, and with it the goal of three years of struggle. If he dropped food, he wilfully and perhaps selfishly jeopardized the lives of his three companions and abandoned his own stern code of plan and preparation. A quick glance at his men convinced him that they felt as he did. The trap door in the fuselage was opened and two bags of food dropped. Lightened by 250 pounds, the plane rose, cleared the pass, and winged south at ninety knots.

A few hours later they were over the pole—located in a white, featureless plain that stretched without interruption to a circular horizon, unspectacular, almost unworthy of comment. Photographs were taken, flags were dropped, and the big tri-motor swung for home. "One gets there," Byrd said, "and that is about all there is for the telling. It is the effort to get there that counts. We put the pole behind us and raced for home."

In McKinley's camera was a continuous record of the flight, newly discovered landscapes and horizons permanently fixed on film, a picture of bleak grandeur and desolation that pioneers, bound to the surface, could only hint at. Once more man's knowledge and understanding of the antarctic was increased by a giant step. And once more Byrd was a hero, but not without help.

The other arms of his enormous expedition carried out an unprecedented scientific program. Other exploratory flights were made, new land was discovered to the east of Little America, a geological journey was made to the Queen Maud Mountains with dog team and sledge. Above all, experience and familiarity were gained which led to the resolve by Byrd and many of his men that there must be another expedition.

Three years later (1933), he was back, bigger, stronger, and better equipped. He had three new aircraft and a wingless whirligig called an Autogiro (now obsolete and effectively replaced by the helicopter). He left no device untried if it gave promise of increasing the efficiency of his explorations. On the ground he equipped himself with five tractors and 153 dogs. (The snowmobile had failed on the first expedition, but dogs were beginning to give way to machines anyhow.)

If this expedition was less spectacular than the first, it was the more fruitful in its results. The explanation might be that for the first time Byrd did not have one of

Citroën tractor, first successful oversnow motor vehicle, used by Byrd on his second antarctic expedition.

National Archives

the earth's poles in his plans to distract him. His mapping plane was a big two-winged Curtis craft known as the "Condor." Hopelessly old-fashioned by present day standards, it was then the ideal exploring instrument. It was equipped with both pontoons and skis, had extra fuel tanks for long-range flights, special ports for the aerial camera, two-way radio, unobstructed vision from the fuselage windows, 9½-ton carrying capacity so that adequate survey and survival gear could be carried, and dump valves so that gasoline could be released quickly in the event of a crash landing.

In this craft Byrd made sweeps over land and sea, penetrating long-neglected white spots on the map that were bounded by Captain Cook's track of one hundred and fifty years before. The total area brought into vision by all exploring parties, ground and air, was 450,000 square miles. Of this 290,000 square miles had never before been seen by man.

On his return, Byrd was not satisfied. He was concerned not with what he had done, but with what remained to do. He pressed relentlessly for another expedition, and by 1939 men and materials had begun to collect. At the same time the United States Government abandoned its long-standing attitude of disinterest in the antarctic. The two joined forces, and on the eve of World War II the United States Antarctic Service was formed with Byrd, now an admiral on the Navy retired list, at its head.

The Little America site was occupied for the third time, and from here an exploring flight was made to the Great Antarctic Horst. The face of this thousand-mile rampart was traversed from Shackleton's Beardmore to Amundsen's Axel Heiberg, and many new geographical features were discovered. Meanwhile another base was established ninety degrees to the east on the western coast of Palmer-Graham Land. From here a plane made sweeps into the little-known land at the base of the peninsula. The vast area between these widely separated points Byrd attacked from the sea, flying from his ship in a seaplane. The result: a new coastline which stretched as far as from Boston to Miami.

For Byrd there followed a turn of wartime duty in warmer fields, but always the old enthusiasm for the horizon and beyond burned brightly. Ideas churned in his mind, big plans took form, his energy seemed inexhaustible. When once again the world took up normal pursuits, Byrd headed south. In 1946 he was placed in joint command, with Rear Admiral Richard H. Cruzen, of a U. S. Navy expedition to antarctic waters. It was the biggest assault yet on the southern continent. The task force numbered thirteen ships, including two seaplane tenders, two ice breakers, supply ships, a submarine, and the aircraft carrier *Philippine Sea*. The aerial arm of the operation consisted of three PBM seaplanes with each tender, a Norseman bushplane for scouting jobs, a helicopter, and six R4D's.

The R4D is the Navy's version of the Douglas DC-3, a large, rugged, two-engined plane that had gained world fame as a hauler of civilian passengers and freight. Each aircraft carried trimetrogon mapping gear—a battery of three cameras, one pointing straight down, the other two at angles to either side, so that a single exposure of film would include both horizons.

A fourth camera photographed a clock and other recording devices; a fifth was part of the radio altimeter apparatus and continuously recorded the plane's altitude above the ground. The shutters of the mapping cameras were tripped several times a minute by an automatic device whose frequency depended on the altitude and speed of the plane. A single flight with this array of equipment could photograph a strip 850 miles long and 70 miles wide—100,000 square miles.

But not all problems could be solved so impressively. None of the naval vessels was of a type suited for antarctic operations. Though the ice breakers would be of assistance, getting through the ice pack presented dangers. Ice breakers themselves were new in these waters, and part of the operational objective was to give crews needed experience. The *Philippine Sea* could not even attempt to penetrate the pack; she was too valuable and her broad steel sides too vulnerable.

The R4D's would take off from the flight deck and establish a flight base at Byrd's old camp—now Little America IV. To accomplish this, the planes were fitted with both wheels *and* skis. The wheels projected three inches below the skis through slots cut in the center. This would enable them to roll on the carrier deck, and yet they would not interfere with the action of the skis when the landing was made on the snow surface of the Ross Ice Shelf. At least so it was hoped, for the fine scheme had not yet been tried!

No plane as big as the R4D had ever taken off from a carrier, and this gave rise to further problems. With a wingspan too great to clear the island, only half the flight deck could be used, and the take-off would have to be assisted with rocket bottles fixed under the wings. Once on the ice, could these heavy craft take off again on skis? It had never been tried before. When the task force approached Antarctica there were, as Byrd expressed it, "a number of rivers to cross."

On a day in January (1947) the *Philippine Sea* turned into the wind eight hundred miles out in the Ross Sea and went full ahead at thirty knots. The first R4D, Commander William M. Hawkes, pilot, rolled down the four-hundred-foot deck. To Byrd it looked pitifully short for a plane that ordinarily required a 2,500-foot runway. Then the rocket bottles cut in with a deafening roar. The deck fell away, and "I knew that we had made it." The landing at Little America was rough enough to capsize most planes, Byrd recounted, but safe for them. The other ships followed without incident.

Finally, in early February, came the first take-off. The weight of the planes had compacted the snow under the skis into ice. Leading Pilot Hawkes opened the throttles to full power. Nothing budged. Men on the snow rocked the plane from the wingtips to loosen the frozen skis; nothing happened. Planks were used to pry at the skis; suddenly they loosened, engines screamed, the ship moved, the rocket bottles cut loose, and the R4D literally shot off the snow. The last "river" had been crossed and the whole operation promised to be eminently successful.

Twenty-nine discovery flights were made into the sprawling, upheaved, unknown country of the Great Antarctic Horst, where a score and more topographic features sprang into view—glaciers, ice sheets, peaks and ranges; into the Rockefeller Mountains, discovered by Byrd in '29 but still incompletely mapped; across the "empty" reaches of the Ross Ice Shelf that no man had seen; along the edge of the Shelf to add another chapter to its hundred-year history of advance and retreat; and once again to the south pole—and beyond, into the absolute blank of the polar plateau.

It was a magnificent achievement, a *tour de force,* and yet it was only part of the total operation. To the east a seaplane group under Captain George Dufek criss-crossed the coast and offshore, filling in gaps in previous mapping flights. To the west Captain Charles A. Bond took his group through 140 degrees of longitude, from the Balleny Islands to Queen Maud Land, surveying with accuracy a total of 1,500 miles of unmapped coastline.

Above this solid piece of work rose the unexpected discovery of an "oasis" area five miles behind the coast, near the 100th meridian. It was a three-hundred-square-mile, ice-free, snow-free anomaly of brown hills (lifeless) and blue lakes (rich in algae) in the midst of a white desert.

The algae were a further point of interest. In general these are microscopic unicellular plants which comprise the green scum found in ponds in warmer climates. In the antarctic oasis area at least three varieties were found— blue, blue-green, and red, the blue representing the lowest stage of development in this primitive form of plant life, and red the highest. We can only speculate on the significance of these living organisms which dwell the year round within the continental perimeter.

It has been suggested that they are the beginnings of independent life in the antarctic environment, which is nominally lifeless. If this is the case, perhaps we are being provided with a view of events which took place over the earth as a whole in the distant past. On the other hand, the algae may be the last rugged remnants of a richer antarctic life that has now all but perished in the cold environment—thus providing us with a view of life in the remote future when the earth as a whole may become cold. If the latter is more reasonable, it is less probable, for the evidence of astronomy indicates that life on earth will end as a result of excessive heat before the final cooling off.

The reason why the oasis area is ice-free is another antarctic problem. One theory is that vulcanism deep beneath the surface provides sufficient heat to prevent the accumulation of snow. But there is no evidence for this,

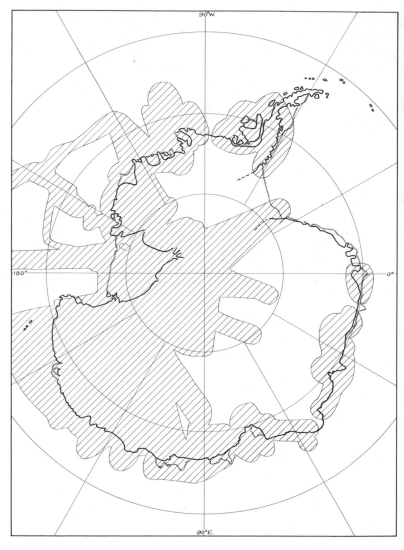

The aerial explorations of Richard E. Byrd; shaded area shows regions viewed during five major expeditions, 1928-56.

and the presence of morain material deposited by glaciers shows that the region was once ice covered. Is it possible that the brown rocks of the exposed hills absorb and store enough heat during the summer to prevent snow accumulation during the winter? Or do prevailing winds simply sweep the region clean?

Whatever the answers to these fundamental questions, for the public the novel oasis area was the most important geographical discovery of the expedition. To geographers and mapmakers, who for twenty years had watched Antarctica take shape under their eyes, it was a mighty cap to Byrd's restless, searching, fruitful career.

It would be unfair and untrue to create the impression that Byrd singlehandedly unveiled the antarctic from the air. He had capable companions on all his expeditions ("Nothing could have been accomplished without these fine men.") and there were capable companion expeditions in the field with him, adding their own important pieces to the antarctic mosaic. John Rymill's British Graham-Land Expedition had used aircraft in its explorations; so also had Australia's Sir Douglas Mawson, Lars Christensen, Riiser-Larsen; the American, Lincoln Ellsworth, flew from Graham-Land to the Bay of Whales in 1936, the first air crossing of the continent, a brilliant, nervy feat, with four ice-cap landings on the way.

Truly they had not done less than Byrd. But who had done more, who had campaigned ceaselessly for twenty years for a single cause, burning up life's energies, growing gray, thin, and even frail? And who had come out of the south with such overwhelming results? Byrd had earned commendation, which he got from every quarter of the globe, and a rest, which he did not get.

11

Operation Deepfreeze:
Plan and Preparation

DURING 1955-56 Byrd was called south once again to bring his experience to bear on a new antarctic scheme, an enterprise so grandiose that even his great scope could not encompass it all. The mission was appropriately named Operation Deepfreeze. It was to be carried out by a large naval task force under the direct command of Rear Admiral George Dufek, a good and capable leader on two of Byrd's previous expeditions.

The purpose of Deepfreeze was to establish on the antarctic continent seven scientific stations to be operated by United States scientists during the International Geophysical Year. This program was a combined effort of the scientists of many nations to study the physical problems of the whole earth, with particular attention devoted to Antarctica. The United States scientific stations were to be located at Little America (the fifth time this famous site would be occupied), in the interior of Marie Byrd Land, on the Weddell coast, on the Wilkes coast, and at the south pole.

No base had ever been built far from the coast, and in the early stages the south pole station was voted least likely to succeed. In addition a station was to be built at Cape Hallett on the Ross Sea and manned jointly with New Zealand, and a center of operations was to be built on McMurdo Sound. The seven stations were not to be antarctic camps in the traditional sense. They were to be

built and equipped so that scientists not necessarily overcome by Antarctica's charms could work on their particular scientific problems in relative comfort and ease. The
problems of construction and supply were therefore new
and difficult.

During the first season, Admiral Dufek's task force consisted of two freighters, three ice breakers—including the
then-new *U.S.S. Glacier*—a tanker, a scouting air arm
made up of four single-engine Otter bush planes and
three helicopters, and a principal exploring and trans-
porting air arm consisting of two P2V Neptunes, two
R4D's, two Albatross triphibians—supposedly able to
operate on land, water, or ice—and two four-engine R5D's,
the Navy version of the Douglas DC-4, which would
operate from a land base in New Zealand. The task force
set a new high in the abundance of flying and floating
"hardware" devoted to antarctic operations.

The flight from New Zealand was a new undertaking,
for no previous attempts had ever been made to make the
hop from temperate lands directly to the antarctic. The
distance was not excessive—2,230 miles—but the weather
at the far end could quickly change from fair to foul. The
ice breakers *Glacier* and *Edisto* steamed south to establish a foothold camp and prepare an airstrip.

The strip was laid on the thick ice of McMurdo Sound
near the old bases of Scott and Shackleton. Its backdrop
was the 13,000-foot snow-whitened cone of Mt. Erebus.
In mid-December (1955) all seemed in readiness, including the weather. Along the flight path ships were stationed
at 250-mile intervals so that there would be a chance for
rescue in the event of a forced landing. Dufek gave the
order for the historic, pioneering flight to take off.

A hundred miles out, the Albatrosses turned back because of strong headwinds and high fuel consumption.

Later the R4D's turned back for the same reason, but only a few miles short of the point of no return. The long-range Neptunes and R5D's continued on their way. "They were on their own. Only one airfield for them now—the ice runway at McMurdo."

The ski-equipped Neptunes landed first, without incident. Then came the R5D's, not on skis but on wheels. No available ski undercarriage was strong enough to support these heavy planes, so the runway had to be specially prepared and compacted, with techniques developed by the U.S. Air Force on the Greenland ice cap. The big ships touched, spewed up snow, rolled to an easy stop. "Routine," the pilots murmured as they emerged with their duffle.

Confident now that an airlift from New Zealand would be successful, Dufek set about digging in at his two principal bases. Leaving half his force to unload at McMurdo Sound, he sailed eastward in the *Glacier* for the Bay of Whales. But this feature of historical note had all but disappeared.

In its inexorable movement the ice shelf had squeezed together the ice caps that formed the headlands of the bay; much ice had broken off and drifted away. Helicopter reconnaissance showed it unsuitable as a station site. Remnants of Little America IV were seen imbedded in the seaward edge of the ice front. Byrd disembarked to prowl his old haunts. "I'm mayor of this place!" he joked. The tops of the steel radio towers of the old Little America I projected six feet above the surface of the snow. In 1928 they had been seventy feet high—convincing evidence of the thickness of the snow that blankets the ice shelf each year.

The force sailed on. Thirty miles to the east was another semipermanent indentation in the ice front: Kainan

Bay. Here more suitable conditions were found for the unloading of heavy cargo, and soon Little America V began the metamorphosis from a plan on paper to a village of red-walled houses under the midnight sun.

Off-loading a ship in the antarctic has never been easy. Bare shores and bluebottle flies appear in Antarctica with equal abundance. The best that can be hoped for is a sheltered mooring in a bay or sound where there is protection from the ocean swells and the sea ice is strong enough to support temporarily the cargo that is placed upon it. All the cargo must then be moved by men and machines (dogs in the old days) from the sea ice to safer high ground.

Vessel unloading at Kainan Bay during Operation Deepfreeze.

Official U.S. Navy Photo

The great risk is that even thick old sea ice may suddenly and unaccountably break, depositing men and matériel into the water. The difficulties are much greater if the unloading is to be done on shelf ice where, as in the case of the Ross Shelf, the seaway edge may be an ice cliff two hundred feet high. The unloading site must then also provide an eroded section of the ice cliff in which a negotiable trail to the top can be cut.

Kainan Bay had all these necessary provisions. But when Dufek arrived with his force the bay was so solidly frozen over that his cargo ships could not enter. It was for precisely this kind of problem that the ice breakers had been brought south. These ships were not new in the world, having been used by Russia in the arctic for over fifty years, but they were new in the antarctic and had been first used during Byrd's 1947 expedition.

The icebreaker is an especially strong, especially powerful, round-bottomed ship. The round bottom, in theory, prevents the ice from getting a vise-like grip on the hull; if such should be threatened the ice jaws will slip off at the same time, causing the vessel to rise and escape. More important, however, to modern ice-breaker technique, is the brute strength of the hull and engines.

In action the ice breaker is driven under full power toward the ice, not to cause a head-on collision—which would damage even the strongest ship and have little effect on the ice—but to ride the bow up and onto the ice. To make this maneuver possible, the forefoot is much cut away and sloping, the forward hull resembling the front end of a toboggan. This subtle refinement, all but invisible above the water line, is highly effective. Although possessing great lateral strength, the thickest sea ice cracks when the weight of an ice breaker bears down from above.

The *Glacier* was on her maiden voyage; she was the newest and best of the Navy's ice ships. In addition to the usual features she was equipped with a heeling tank system that could shift 140,000 gallons of liquid ballast (fuel or water) from one side of the vessel to the other and back again in three minutes. Thus if she should become mildly stuck, the *Glacier* was prepared to wriggle free. With ten diesel engines developing 20,000 horsepower, and a displacement of 8,625 tons, she was capable of crushing solid pack ice fifteen feet thick.

This powerful vessel steamed into Kainan Bay. The order to "stand by for ramming ice" was passed over the ship's loudspeaker system, and every man on board grabbed some nearby support to keep his feet during the jolting blows. For twenty-four hours the battle raged, and in that time the ice breaker cut and cleared out of the bay

U.S.S. Glacier breaking her way through light sea ice in McMurdo Sound.

Official U.S. Navy Photo

a slip two miles long and a mile wide, removing in the process four million tons of ice. Giant strides forward in man's journey to the heart of the antarctic!

Entering the harbor the *Glacier* had manufactured, the cargo vessels moored snugly to the ice by means of "deadmen." These are strong billets of timber with a loop of wire or rope around the middle. A trench is dug in the ice, the deadman dropped in, and water poured on top. When this freezes the whole becomes a species of immovable object. The ship's lines are fastened to the deadman by a loop-and-toggle arrangement, so that in an emergency a single blow with a mallet releases the mooring.

As soon as the cargo was lowered to the fast bay ice, it was hauled away to the site of Little America V, on the surface of the ice shelf five miles away. This arduous task that the pioneers had accomplished with dogs was now done by a fleet of mechanized apparatus: weasels, Sno-Cats, fork-lifts, and Caterpillar tractors. Men worked the clock around in two shifts, the midnight sun providing all necessary illumination.

In addition to the material required for the IGY Little America Station, there was a roughly equal amount (five hundred tons) required for IGY Byrd Station to be built in the middle of Marie Byrd Land four hundred and fifty miles away. The station would be reached and supplied by tractor train, an undertaking second to none in antarctic logistics. As the off-loading continued, construction crews commenced building the permanent station structures—for the most part, buildings that had been prefabricated in the United States and needed only to be set on foundations and bolted together at the site. Streets and avenues were tramped out in the snow, and scientific laboratories, garages, and antenna arrays were constructed in the "suburbs."

Back at McMurdo Sound a similar process transformed Hut Point into a polar metropolis of thirty-five buildings, including the first church in Antarctica. This base was not to be a scientific station but the center of operations and the jumping-off place for the airlift that would establish the IGY Amundsen-Scott Station at the south pole. The quality of the surface at the pole was unknown; only Amundsen and Scott had seen it, and their reports were fifty years old. Take-offs from the high altitude of the polar plateau (9000 feet) would be difficult, perhaps impossible, for heavily loaded planes. But these were the conditions for freighting in hundreds of tons of supplies, and Admiral Dufek felt, ". . . we had confidence that the job *could* be done." But first, reconnaissance.

In early January, 1956, Marine Lieutenant Colonel H. R. Kolp took off in a four-engined R5D on a flight that took him to the pole. He circled, dropped to within five hundred feet of the surface. His report: ". . . perfectly flat with long gentle snowdrifts like a stationary sea. . . ." It looked promising, but another flight was made. In the rear compartment rode Richard Byrd on his third trip to the bottom of the world.

It was a poignant moment for the Admiral of the Ends of the Earth, as he gazed down on the scene of his early adventure in the Ford tri-motor with a handful of men. No food bags to be jettisoned here in a desperate fight to gain altitude. On the contrary, there were pork chops and fried potatoes for lunch, hot tea at regular intervals. "Quite a difference," Byrd observed (delighting in or regretting the tremendous progress in exploration that had removed much of the thrill?). As the craft dipped low, he concluded from the crisscross pattern of the *sastrugi* that the surface was firm and would support a landing.

Other flights were made. Dufek's big planes roared

deep into the "outback" that lay behind Wilkes Land.
Flights were aimed at the Pole of Inaccessibility. Everywhere the results were the same: the interior was a gently
sloping ice dome over 11,000 feet high, rippled slightly
by the wind but otherwise blank. A long pioneering flight
was made by Captain William ("Trigger") Hawkes, from
McMurdo Sound to the Weddell Sea and back, passing
over the south pole enroute.

Could the snowbound Scott or even the swift Amundsen ever have conceived such traffic in the forsaken lands
they knew? The 3,200-mile flight was the longest yet made
in Antarctica. Along the way mountains were seen thrust-
ing up through the thick polar cap, the first hint that
there was something in the deep interior besides ice.

When the flights were finished it was mid-January. The
southern summer was well advanced; the ice of the Mc-
Murdo landing strip was deteriorating. Dufek declared
the flying season closed. The rewards were rich: two bases
built, a million square miles of new territory explored,
and a store of flying experience for next year.

September, 1956: Dufek was back at McMurdo in the
vanguard of an imposing new force—more ships, more
planes, more men. "For two years our men had planned
and labored. In our minds the symbol of our greatest
triumph would be a successful landing by plane at the
south pole. . . . Would we be successful?"

The airlift from New Zealand was increased in size. In
addition to the usual Neptunes, R4D's, and R5D's, Dufek
had secured from the U.S. Air Force eight C-124 Globemasters, huge double-decker giants with a payload capacity of twenty-three tons. Their function was to parachute five hundred tons of matériel at the pole, a difficult
feat but necessary because the big ships were too heavy to
land on a snow surface.

The airlift was a success, but not without penalty. The very first Neptune to approach McMurdo from New Zealand ran into flukey weather too late to turn back. Approaching the ice strip in heavy overcast, the pilot lost control; the plane cartwheeled and crashed. Four men were killed and three injured. The inflexible IGY schedule, the strong sense of Navy duty, gradually dispersed the gloom over this tragedy, but not the realization that the antarctic can still lash out with dangerous weapons.

As the supplies piled up at McMurdo, preparations for the second airlift to the south pole progressed. A halfway depot was established at the base of the mountains of the Horst. Ski-equipped planes on the pole run could land here for refuelling. In the event of a crash landing survivors could head for it. When all plans and precautions had been put into effect Dufek ordered the final reconnaissance: a landing at the pole.

The pioneer plane was an R4D, the reliable veteran of so many ski landings. On its nose it bore the whimsical Spanish name *Que Sera Sera* ("Whatever will be, will be"). In the pilot's seat for this historic flight was Commander Conrad Shinn; his co-pilot was the experienced and capable Trigger Hawkes. In the compartment was survival gear, food for fourteen days, and many cameras sent along by newsmen and enthusiasts who wanted a record of the event.

The take-off was almost anti-climactic, for a flight in the direction of the pole had by now begun to assume some of the aspects of a milk run—almost. The track lay parallel to the Horst, then turned poleward over the Beardmore. As Dufek flew he jotted down his impressions. Two hours away from the pole he wrote: "_____ is at the hot plate brewing some coffee and making me a toasted-cheese sandwich."

Once more the gap closed. With his target below, pilot Shinn flew in a square to enable his navigators to check position. He was within two thousand yards of the pole. He dropped, making three passes over the surface, each lower than the preceding one. Nothing untoward came into view. He eased down for the final run. The R4D touched, bumped as the skis rode on the hard ripples of snow, slid to a stop.

Dufek was first out. "It was like stepping out into a new world." The crew tumbled after, their voices the first to be heard here in forty-four years. The wind blew at ten miles per hour. The temperature was fifty-eight degrees below zero. Faces quickly froze, fingers stiffened, cameras lucklessly refused to function. To this same point it took Scott weeks to struggle. The stamina of the pioneers seemed scarcely credible.

Que Sera Sera, first airplane to land at the south pole.

Dufek tried to drive a flag into the snow; it was too hard. A radar reflector was set up to make future navigation easier. The engines of the plane ominously began to drip oil. It was time to leave. Shinn fired eight rocket bottles to break the skis loose, four more to reach take-off speed, the last three to lift the plane into the thin air. Man's third visit to the uttermost point of the earth had occupied forty-nine minutes.

Dufek accepted his triumph with humility. He thanked his men and the good fortune they had met. He had, however, achieved a notable "first." He had demonstrated the feasibility of landing aircraft at the pole; he had guaranteed the success of the final phase of Deepfreeze. A month was spent waiting. When milder weather came in November, a ski-equipped plane flew in a pioneer party of constructors. An accompanying Globemaster parachuted their heavy equipment: Weasel, sledges, timber, food and fuel. A temporary camp sprang up. The exact location of the south pole was determined. Then began the giant assault.

It was on a scale heretofore unknown. It was an invasion of an inanimate enemy. The Globemasters dropped the makings of a small city: prefabricated buildings, electric-light plants, telephone systems, snow melters, bed and board for several score men, scientific instruments for the diverse activities of the IGY party, 55,000 gallons of fuel, a D-2 Caterpillar tractor—the usual mass of technical and polar whatnots that explorers need, which in the past had erupted from the hulls of ships and now streamed on varicolored nylon parachutes from the bellies of giant aircraft.

Timber was free-dropped, without a parachute. When it hit, snow spewed up as if a bomb had exploded (and marshaling crews had to dig for hours to extricate the buried boards). One tractor came down on a parachute which failed to open. The machine buried itself forty-five feet in the snow, a total wreck. The planes came in several flights a day, bringing an average of ten tons each. The total payload for the entire operation was 760 tons.

In a period of weeks the helter-skelter construction camp became an orderly scientific station. The work of the constructors lessened and was then eclipsed by the scientists, who set up laboratories, began observations. The amenities of civilization began to flow. Laundry and showers with running hot water. Radio-telephone service to any spot on earth, including home. Hi-fi records for leisure-time listening. A post office for processing the mail of thousands of stamp collectors. Steak, ham, and turkey, not for holidays but for everyday fare. All in the actual shadow of the south pole, which had been waggishly marked with an orange-and-black-striped barber pole.

In December the work drew to a close; Dufek's toughest assignment was successfully concluded. The last nail was hammered, the last bolt tightened. The constructors departed, leaving a party of eighteen scientists and Navy personnel to spend man's first winter at the pole. "Beyond the strange and alluring beauty of the mountain ranges . . . lies this high plateau of frozen solitude. What are the secrets that men will learn from it in years to come?" It was the mission of the scientists to find out.

12

IGY: The Combined Assault

GEOPHYSICS IS AN omnibus science that studies the earth on the largest scale. Its province extends from the molten center of the planet, through the crust and atmosphere, into nearby space and beyond. It is a science that does not progress rapidly in the laboratory; it requires observations of phenomena at stations all across the globe, in deserts and on mountain tops, in the middle of oceans and ice caps, at the equator and poles, in orbiting satellites a thousand miles above the earth's surface.

Global scientific programs are not easy to organize. They require the cooperation of many nations, of some that are not friendly to each other. But the unifying spirit of science is strong, and by 1950 plans were laid. Eight years later a world-wide geophysical program was an accomplished fact. The program was called the International Geophysical Year, forever after abbreviated to IGY. It extended from July, 1957 to December, 1958, and during its progress geophysics quickly achieved a status that had been denied it during the preceding half century.

The scientists of sixty-six nations participated in a world-wide study program in eleven major areas: 1—the measurement of the earth's gravity, 2—the exact determination of the latitude and longitude of the continents, 3—seismology (the study of earth structure by means of earthquake waves), 4—glaciology, 5—oceanography, 6—meteorology, 7—solar activity, 8—cosmic rays, 9—earth magnetism, 10—the aurora (northern and southern lights), and 11—the ionosphere (a high-altitude electrified layer of the atmosphere).

Several sciences, such as glaciology and meteorology, were directly related to the antarctic, for most of the world's ice and perhaps much of its weather is manufactured there. But because Antarctica was still a large and little known region of the earth, a special program was organized so that this region would receive intensive study. Twelve nations participated in the IGY antarctic program: Argentina, Australia, Belgium, Chile, France, Japan, New Zealand, Norway, South Africa, the United Kingdom, the United States, and the Soviet Union. Among them, thirty-eight new scientific stations were constructed and manned.

Individual national efforts varied from a single station, such as Japan's Showa Station on the Prince Harald Coast, to the fifteen stations manned by Great Britain. Locations varied from Australia's Macquarie Island Station, lying outside the Antarctic Convergence and therefore of a decidedly sub-antarctic character, to the United States Amundsen-Scott Station, located at the south pole. The Soviet Union established five stations on the ice cap (compared with two for the U.S. and one for Great Britain). One of these, Sovietskaya Station, was in the vicinity of the Pole of Inaccessibility, and its build-up and support involved difficulties no less formidable than those encountered during Operation Deepfreeze.

At all stations a rigorous round of scientific observations was carried out by a staff consisting at the minimum of a physicist, a glaciologist, a meteorologist, and certain supernumeraries for communications, photography, engine repairs, and general maintenance. Many phenomena had to be studied synoptically. That is, a number of observations must be made at many different places but all

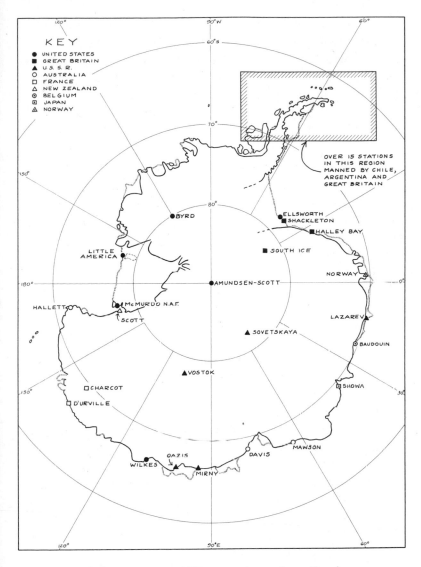

KEY
● UNITED STATES
■ GREAT BRITAIN
▲ U.S.S.R.
○ AUSTRALIA
□ FRANCE
△ NEW ZEALAND
⊙ BELGIUM
⊡ JAPAN
⍓ NORWAY

120°   90°W   60°
60°S
70°

OVER 15 STATIONS
IN THIS REGION
MANNED BY CHILE,
ARGENTINA AND
GREAT BRITAIN

150°
80°
●BYRD
●ELLSWORTH
■SHACKLETON
■HALLEY BAY
LITTLE
AMERICA
■ SOUTH ICE
NORWAY
180°
●AMUNDSEN-SCOTT   0°
HALLETT
●McMURDO N.A.F.
△SCOTT
LAZAREV
▲SOVETSKAYA
⊙BAUDOUIN
▲VOSTOK
□CHARCOT
□D'URVILLE
⊡SHOWA   30°
150°
MAWSON
OAZIS
DAVIS
●WILKES   ▲MIRNY
120°   50°E   60°

Some of the important IGY artarctic stations. Twelve par-
ticipating nations manned a total of 58 stations.

at the same time, so that when the data are assembled
a worldwide picture at a given instant is achieved.

The weather, earth magnetism, and the aurora, for ex-
ample, require synoptic observations for fruitful study.
To facilitate the collection of meteorological data, all sta-
tions were linked in a continent-wide radio net called
Weather Central. The headquarters of the net was located
at Little America and was operated by scientists from
Argentina, Australia, France, the United States, and the
Soviet Union.

Certain programs went beyond mere observation and
included the mounting of extensive over-the-snow journeys called "traverses." The chief objectives of the traverses were geographical exploration and seismic sounding of the ice to determine the subglacial features of the
continent, neither of which can be accomplished from a
fixed point. The traverses were the high point of the IGY
antarctic program; they achieved signal results and afforded a modicum of adventure in a land where adventure was seen to be slipping out the back way.

From Little America V a looping traverse of the Ross
Ice Shelf was made, the first extensive examination of
this much-discussed feature. From Byrd Station a 1,026-
mile traverse was made to the mountains in eastern Marie
Byrd Land. From Shackleton Station on the Weddell Sea
coast a British party crossed the continent. Soviet scientists performed an over-the-snow tour that began at Vostok
Station, zigzagged first to the south pole, then to the Pole
of Inaccessibility.

While all these activities transpired on the surface of
the continent, many support and exploratory flights were
made through her skies. The airplane became the good
right arm of the traversing parties, most of which received
supplies by air. Two U.S. Air Force planes flew from

Ushuaia at the southern tip of South America to Ellsworth Station on the Weddell coast. It was the first time these two continents had been linked by air. Whenever free of their tasks of support and supply, the various expedition ships undertook oceanographical cruises, probing the waters that surround the continent in an endeavor to throw light on antarctic problems from that quarter.

At the ground stations the meteorologists had their standard assortment of thermometers, barometers, anemometers, precipitation gauges. But gone were the days of dressing in furs and battling the blizzard to reach the instrument screen, of irritating struggles with solidified ink and frozen clockworks. The new instruments were electrical and their readings were telemetered to self-recording meters inside station quarters.

There were also new quantities to be measured; the duration of sunshine, the net flow of radiation at the surface—that is, the amount of heat received directly from the sun—the heat received from clouds and the surrounding atmosphere, and the energy radiated by the surface materials back into the atmosphere. Such data were aimed at the very basic problem of whether the ice cap is warming or cooling, whether the quantity of ice is increasing (which seems unlikely), decreasing, or in a state of mass equilibrium (accumulation exactly balanced by ablation).

Attention was directed to the upper atmosphere, where, it is increasingly recognized, lies the key to the behavior of surface air and to the grand scheme of atmospheric circulation over the whole globe. Data from here were got by the usual balloons equipped with radiosonde gear for transmitting it to ground stations, or from very high altitudes by means of "rockoons"—a rocket and balloon combination in which the balloon carries a rocket to a height of about twelve miles. At that point the rocket fires and carries its load of telemetering instruments to a height of sixty miles or more. To study the aurora, an ultra-high atmospheric phenomenon, the Amundsen-Scott Station was equipped with a plastic dome from which whole-sky photographs could be taken, and spectrographic apparatus for analyzing the faint auroral light.

The attention of the glaciologists was directed downward, to the ice of a then-unknown thickness beneath their feet. Of the several methods of measuring ice thickness, the seismic method yields the most accurate results. It makes use of the familiar echo principle which bounces a shout back to us from a mountainside. In seismic sounding an explosion is used instead of a shout, and the function of the mountainside is performed by the rock floor on which the ice rests. The echo is detected by a seismograph, the same instrument used to detect the vibrational waves caused by earthquakes.

United States Ellsworth Station on the Weddell Sea under construction.

Official U.S. Navy Photo

If the velocity of the waves set up by the explosion is known, and also the time between the explosion and the return of the echo, it is a fairly simple matter to calculate how far the waves have traveled and thus how deep the ice is. In practice, however, the time interval is very short, and the correct reflected wave must be sorted out from a multitude of extraneous waves that are generated at the same time, thus adding complexities. But the equipment is portable and a single sounding takes only a few hours. The traverse parties made many soundings over many parts of the ice cap, and the IGY scientists were able to delve into matters that were absolute mysteries a few years before.

The simplest means of directly examining the interior of the ice cap is to dig a hole and examine the ice of the walls as you dig. This the modern glaciologist does, but with refined and subtle techniques (above and beyond the shovel and bucket used to clear the hole!). Stakes are driven into the tunnel wall, so that movement within the ice mass may be observed. Thermocouples (electric thermometers) are then inserted in the ice at various depths.

The temperature deep inside a polar glacier is found to be very close to the average yearly temperature of the atmosphere above. Thus a summer reading of interior ice temperatures provides a basis for estimating the winter temperatures in regions that are inaccessible in winter. Samples of the ice are tested for strength and deformation characteristics. Chemical analyses are made to detect dust or other extraneous material. The microscope is used to search for plant spores. Thin sections are cut so that crystal structure may be studied. Some of the ice may even find its way into a melter so that the station personnel may have a supply of hot water.

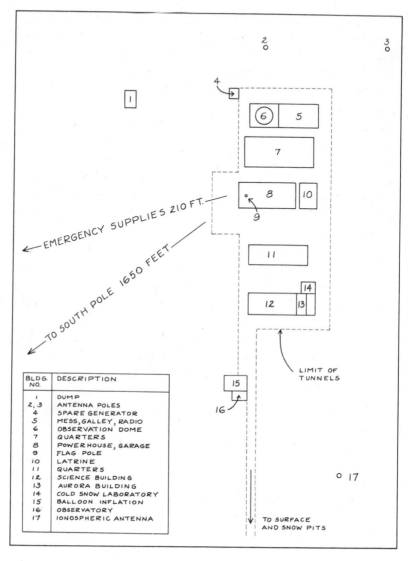

BLDG. NO.	DESCRIPTION
1	DUMP
2, 3	ANTENNA POLES
4	SPARE GENERATOR
5	MESS, GALLEY, RADIO
6	OBSERVATION DOME
7	QUARTERS
8	POWER HOUSE, GARAGE
9	FLAG POLE
10	LATRINE
11	QUARTERS
12	SCIENCE BUILDING
13	AURORA BUILDING
14	COLD SNOW LABORATORY
15	BALLOON INFLATION
16	OBSERVATORY
17	IONOSPHERIC ANTENNA

Plan of United States IGY Amundsen-Scott Station at the south pole, 1958.

But digging tunnels is not only laborious, it has its practical limits. For deep sampling it is quite out of the question, and a core-boring machine is used. This is a device borrowed from the oil industry and modified to suit ice. It drills a hole, but in so doing the cutting tool leaves a central cylindrical section of ice intact, which is retrieved from the hole for examination. In principle it is exactly the same as the kitchen gadget which removes the core from an apple. As core borings may be made to depths of a thousand feet, the technique gives a narrow but deep peek into the remote past of glaciers.

During IGY, provision was made to transport some of the core samples back to the United States, still frozen, where they could be examined in more adequately equipped laboratories. At depths below one thousand feet the release of strains in the ice by the cutting tool causes the core to shatter; also trapped gases are suddenly released, which destroys the sample.

All these efforts, pressed by many nations, constituted an assault on antarctic problems of unprecedented character. The raw data are still being processed, will be studied for years. The results in some of the more obscure disciplines may be years more in sifting down to the layman. But in purely antarctic matters the main lines of the new information have already been laid down.

It appears that (1) Antarctica is, after all, still the coldest place on earth and possibly a little colder than expected; (2) Antarctica is still the world's greatest storehouse of ice and contains much more ice than previously estimated; (3) Antarctica, the white continent and the seventh continent among other names, may not be a continent at all.

Dr. Paul Siple, one of the scientific leaders at IGY

Amundsen-Scott Station, predicted that at the south pole winter temperatures of 120 degrees below zero might be encountered. It was an estimate based on what he knew about summer temperatures (about zero) and the yearly average obtained from the interior of the ice (about sixty below zero). The average temperatures actually recorded during July and August, 1957, usually the coldest months, were seventy-six degrees and seventy-two degrees below zero respectively. This was warmer than expected, though not balmy, for a cup of water dashed into the air freezes before it strikes the ground, and ordinary breathing may injure the delicate tissues of the lungs.

At Little America the average temperature for the year was 11.5 degrees below zero, which was 5½ degrees warmer than in the year 1911, when Amundsen's party recorded temperatures. Records of the various Byrd expeditions show a gradual increase of temperature in the years between. Whether this indicates a real warming up of Antarctica or merely a local fluctuation is uncertain, although the evidence, particularly of ice shrinkage, is on the side of the former.

During September, a month in which moderating temperatures may be expected, Amundsen-Scott Station experienced a "cold snap." The monthly average was down to 79 degrees below zero, and the low for the month was 102.1 below. The following year (1958) when the Russians were established at Sovietskaya Station near the Pole of Inaccessibility, a low of 124 degrees below zero was recorded—the coldest surface temperature yet observed and a few degrees lower than Siple's theoretical prediction. Such a low temperature is partly explained by the continental location of the station, that is, its remoteness from the moderating influence of the sea. But that is not the whole story.

A meteorologist might phrase the question: By what process does Antarctica lose her heat? For to the scientist heat is the fundamental substance of the matter—not cold. The atmosphere receives heat from the sun during the day and loses it by radiation during the night, the coldest hours being just before dawn, when the sun starts its warming action again. The special condition in the antarctic is the elongation of day and night because of the high latitude and the increased opportunity this provides for excessive radiation of heat (cooling) during the dark period.

In actuality the polar night is not six months long. Because of the refraction of the sun's rays by the atmosphere around the curved surface, the longest period of complete darkness extends from May 12th to July 31st, approximately eighty days. But this is only at the exact south pole, and at more northerly points the period of darkness is shorter. Nevertheless, during this time and during the twilight period which precedes and follows, conditions for heat radiation are very good.

It further appears that the most efficient radiation takes place at the snow surface, which forms the lower boundary of the atmosphere. Immediately above the surface the air is warmer, having been warmed by the radiation from below! This condition of warm air overlying cold is a very stable one. It is the temperature inversion previously mentioned, and it prevents the churning up of the lower layers of the atmosphere, which otherwise moderates the cold.

Winds, which are the result of unequal heating and cooling, complicate matters, for they constantly tend to equalize temperatures. It had been thought that in the middle of the dark, radiating ice-cap winds would be light or absent. Such a windless area was discovered, cen-

tered in 1957 over the region of inaccessibility, while at
the south pole there were light winds of up to twenty
miles per hour from the direction of the Weddell Sea.

Snowfall at the south pole was light—only six inches
of net accumulation in one year. It seems incredible that
the enormous mass of the ice cap could have been built
from such light precipitation. But of course this snow
never melts, and Antarctica has had centuries to collect
it. The glaciologist F. Loewe has made a calculation which
shows that to maintain the present rate of iceberg production at the edge of the ice cap, the accumulation on the
entire surface need only be as much as one inch of water.
The water equivalent of snow is highly variable, ranging
from six to thirty inches of snow per one inch of water,
but the observed accumulation is within reasonable agreement with the theoretical requirement.

In the over-all weather picture IGY turned up little
that was absolutely new. The interior of the continent
has long been recognized as an inexhaustible reservoir
of cold air. When this air spills outward and meets the
moist, comparatively warm air over the sea, it gives rise
to turbulence—the raw, stormy weather so characteristic
of the continental fringe. Tracks of storms plotted by
IGY scientists virtually ring the continent throughout the
year.

What the IGY did provide that was new was a network
of weather stations sufficiently scattered and making simultaneous observations, so that for the first time weather
patterns could be predicted. This contributed greatly
to the safety of all operations, particularly flying, and
provided for the first time a comprehensive weather picture of the entire southern hemisphere. For the data to
be of lasting value, however, the stations must be maintained and the observations continued.

In the autumn of man's first winter at the south pole, a team of seismologists set off their charges, disentangled the maze of wavy lines on the recording drum of their seismograph, and concluded that the thickness of the ice under the pole is 8,297 feet. Since the surface elevation at the pole is 9,200 feet above sea level, the ice rests on rock with the modest elevation of 903 feet. It was one of IGY's most brilliant antarctic discoveries, and together with other seismic findings caused major revision in our concept of the continent.

High as Antarctica's mountain fringes may be, the interior is low. It cannot be thought of as a high rock mass covered with a sheet of ice, in the way frosting covers a cake. This was not entirely new under the sun, for exactly the same condition exists in Greenland, which supports the world's second largest ice cap. Here too an early picture of a high ice-capped land had to be revised when seismic soundings showed ice of great thickness resting in a low basin.

What *is* the subglacial nature of Antarctica? In Marie Byrd Land seismic results were, if anything, more surprising. The surface elevation at Byrd Station is 6,000 feet. The thickness of the ice cap was found to be 14,000 feet, the greatest ice thickness ever measured. But the bottom of this ice must therefore lie 3,000 feet *below sea level*. In other words, there is no "land" here; the ice has simply filled a sea and is resting on its bottom.

On the road from Little America to Byrd Station the subglacial rock is entirely below sea level. In the interior of Victoria Land the bedrock is over 3000 feet below sea level. Southwest of Ellsworth Station on the Weddell coast the rock floor is 3,500 feet below sea level. At the French IGY Charcot Station the ice is 9,000 feet thick, and the bedrock lies 3,000 feet below sea level. In the

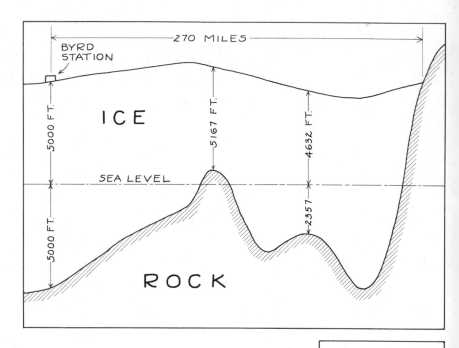

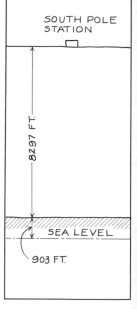

Above: A profile along a traverse into Marie Byrd Land. Most of the "land" is below the level of the sea. Right: A profile at the south pole, a point of modest elevation overlaid by thousands of feet of ice.

coastal region near the Russian Mirny Station the bedrock under the ice was found to be below sea level.

These startling results imply that at best Antarctica is scarred with a patchwork of low spots in which lie some of the planet earth's greatest thicknesses of ice. At worst it may mean that Antarctica is not a continent at all but a group of large islands, a gigantic ice-covered archipelago. Although data from some critical regions is still lacking, there is strong evidence once again that Palmer-Graham Land is an island cut off from the mainland, if we may still use that term, by a deep channel. And the real rock "coast" of Wilkes Land must lie several hundred miles back from the ice edge.

But for those who feel dismay because of the image of a continent being destroyed, there is still hope. The south pole lies above sea level, as does the entire route followed by Sir Vivian Fuchs across Antarctica. Also at IGY Vostok Station, 1,000 miles into the interior of the ice cap, the ice is a formidable 8,700 feet thick, but the underlying rock is 2,300 feet above sea level. The Australian IGY Mawson Station also has "dry" rock under it. A synthesis of these views may be seen in the accompanying map.

Geophysicists have suggested that the lowness of the antarctic rocks is caused by the enormous weight of ice resting on them. It is possible that the crustal rocks have sagged under the load and have sunk into the plastic mantle. In this view, if the ice were to melt the crust will spring upward and restore Antarctica to its continental status. But melting the ice cap would raise ocean levels, which would have the opposite effect. These processes, of course, require millions of years, and although scientists have made bold calculations about water levels and land levels of the remote future, we may never know what the rock face of Antarctica really looks like.

The real Antarctica? A hypothetical map based on recent
seismic explorations. On melting of the ice cap, Antarctica may resemble this.

Core borings to a depth of 1,000 feet show that ice at this level is 1,400 years old. This provides a rough measure for judging the age of the whole ice cap. The bottom layers of the ice in Marie Byrd Land must have fallen as snow as long ago as 19,600 years. This may be an over-simplification, for if the ice cap is in a plastic state, the bottom layers may be much younger, having flowed to their present position from elsewhere. Or they may be older, having long ago been trapped in basins from which there was no escape.

Assuming an average depth of ice of 7,000 feet, which is one-half the maximum depth, and multiplying by the area of Antarctica, which is about 5.3 million square miles, and multiplying further by the density of ice, we arrive at the figure of 29 million billion tons of water in the ice cap. If this were spread uniformly over the oceans of the world, sea level would be raised by some 248 feet. If we have been extravagant in our estimates, we may cut this figure in half.

The resulting 124-foot rise would still be sufficient to flood New York, London, and every other port city in the world, not to mention its effect on continental shore-lines of Antarctica, whose fate will be complicated. The prospect is staggering but not imminent; mankind, if still in existence when the last gram of ice has melted, will have had millions of years to prepare for the deluge.

There has been rather more speculation in the opposite direction, on the past rather than the future, on the possible factors that have brought Antarctica to its present state. The white princess has not always been cold; the discovery of coal and fossil plants indicates beyond doubt that she once enjoyed a warm, even tropical, climate. What brought about such drastic changes in her climatic fortunes?

Temperature is a fundamental element in the solution of the puzzle. In the northern hemisphere it is known that great ice sheets have advanced and retreated four times in recent geological history (up to one million years ago). There is further evidence of major glacial periods in more ancient times, although knowledge of these is less complete. It would appear that there has been a periodic fluctuation of the earth's average temperature.

But cold climate alone is not enough to cause the formation of continental ice sheets. The ice is made of compacted snow, and this must fall from the atmosphere, which implies that at times of active glacier formation there is heavy precipitation. The conditions necessary for this are a *relatively* warm atmosphere for efficient evaporation, and ice-free oceans to serve as a water source. It may be that extreme cold is not required at all, merely *cool summers* to preserve the winter snow until the next season.

Climatologists, geophysicists, and astronomers are not in agreement as to how these somewhat contrary factors should be related in a correct explanation. Astronomers are involved in the matter because one of the simplest explanations is that the heat given off by the sun is not constant. It is true that slight changes in the sun's radiation are observed. During years of sunspot activity, when the solar surface is disturbed, there is a slight decrease in the amount of heat received by the earth. But these changes are too small and of too short duration to be related to the long process of building a continental ice sheet, and in the absence of evidence of more significant changes in the sun's output, scientists have sought explanations elsewhere.

Some climatologists favor a theory that depends on a variation in the transparency of the earth's atmosphere.

Water vapor in the atmosphere, for example, gives rise to a so-called "greenhouse effect." The sun's energy in the form of *light* passes through the atmosphere easily, but the *heat* radiated by the surface of the earth does not pass out again through the water-vapor barrier, thus causing a warming of the lower atmosphere.

Thus far the theory corresponds with observation. But if the amount of water vapor in the air were reduced, this effect would be reduced, and the earth would suffer a lowering of temperature. But what removed the water vapor? The cosmologist F. Hoyle has suggested that periodically the earth passes through clouds of interplanetary dust resulting from the break-up of comets. The dust particles, acting as condensation nuclei for the water vapor, cause it to precipitate ultimately as snow, and cool the atmosphere at the same time!

Along these same lines Dr. Harry Wexler of the U.S. Weather Bureau sees dust in another role but causing the same end result. Dust can also act as a shield, causing the sun's radiation to be reflected rather than transmitted or absorbed. If some agent were to contaminate the atmosphere with a few million million tons of dust, again a cool period might result, but by quite a different process. The eruption of volcanoes might serve the initial purpose. But Wexler himself has pointed out that modern eruptions have not produced enough of the required material to cause a noticeable world-wide effect, and our knowledge of vulcanism in the past is slight.

A very precise theory has been offered by Professor George Gamow of the University of Denver, who thinks that variations in the earth's motions may be the primary cause. The inclination of the earth's axis, which is the cause of the change of seasons, and the earth's nearness to the sun, which has a small but noticeable effect on earth temperatures, both experience gradual changes over great periods of time. Gamow has shown that there have been times when the cooling effects of these changes are "in step" and the combined effects are sufficient to cause the lowering of temperature required for glaciation. Furthermore, his calculations, based on purely astronomical data, yield cold periods at times exactly corresponding with the observed glacial periods in the northern hemisphere.

If we pick our favorite among these diverse theories, we still shall not receive full marks for the problem. All seek primarily to explain the advance of glaciers, but do not specifically account for the fact that Antarctica was, in carboniferous times, a tropical land where teeming jungles thrived. The coal formed from the carbonized remains of the plants that grew in these jungles is found today sandwiched between the sediments of the Antarctic Horst. Antarctica was, therefore, not simply cool, or warm, but *hot*.

One of the most imaginative and consequently most attractive explanations of this state of affairs is the theory of continental drift. First proposed by the Austrian geophysicist Alfred Wegener, the theory presumes that the continents are like great rafts of rock floating on the denser rocks of the earth's mantle, and that in the long history of the earth they have not always been where they are now. It is thought that forces derived from the earth's rotation have caused the continents actually to drift about on the highly viscous layer of subcontinental basalt.

That such a theory is plausible is realized when we look at a map of the world and see that the continents resemble the pieces of a puzzle that once fitted together. The east coasts of the Americas clearly would fit nicely against the west coasts of Europe and Africa. And this can be no mere coincidence, it is argued. A place for Antarctica can be found off Africa's Cape of Good Hope, and this would suffice to give it the requisite tropical climate. There is further evidence in the slight residual magnetism found in Antarctic rocks. The direction of this magnetism indicates that the south magnetic pole, and presumably Antarctica, once could have been in the assigned position.

The flaw is that calculations show the resistance encountered by a continent drifting through a mass of plastic basalt is many thousands times greater than the forces available for causing the drift. Thus, if any drift occurred, it must have been at a time when the basalt layer in which the continents are presently imbedded was in a *molten* state. This in turn could occur only when the young earth was still cooling—long before any life appeared. Despite the perplexing evidence of rock magnetism and convincing puzzle-piece outlines, we must conclude that Antarctica has been in her present position throughout geologic history as recorded by sedimentary rocks.

This is by no means the end of theories on climatic change and glacial variations. They would fill several books. But until the matter is settled, it is a good place to stop this long and rather technical discourse and take up once more man's more immediate struggles with the antarctic environment.

13

Midcentury Traverses

Two GENERATIONS had passed and with them many changes had been rung into antarctic technology, but the main features of the plan to cross Antarctica during the IGY remained unchanged. A principal British party under Vivian E. Fuchs would advance toward the interior from a base (IGY Shackleton Station) on the Weddell Sea coast; a support party of New Zealanders would advance from a base on the Ross Sea coast (IGY Scott Station); the two would meet somewhere on the plateau, probably in the vicinity of the pole, and finish the journey together. There could be no better tribute to Sir Ernest Shackleton, the man who had originally conceived, boldly attempted, and gallantly failed in the last grand journey forty years before.

Dr. Fuchs was an unprofessorial professor of geology at Cambridge University, who entertained more than an academic interest in the world; he early hungered for adventure, and led an expedition to Greenland when he was 21. In subsequent years he explored in West Africa, and after World War II he served a second polar apprenticeship on survey expeditions to British antarctic territories. When he assumed command of the Commonwealth Trans-Antarctic Expedition he was nearing his fiftieth birthday, tough and supple as a polythene wand.

His younger second-in-command, who led the Ross Sea party, was New Zealander Sir Edmund Hillary. He had been a member of the first party to scale Mount

Everest, possessed all the qualifications demanded by this arduous achievement, was six feet four inches tall, and faced the special antarctic problem of procuring boots large enough to fit his oversized feet. The solution was a pair of huge black objects which the newspapers compared with Noah's Ark.

At heart Fuchs was a "dog man," for he used these animals extensively in his survey work and was convinced of their value for short, lightly equipped thrusts. But the transantarctic expedition was not to be short, nor would it go lightly equipped. Shackleton had planned to use dogs and *might* have made it; Fuchs did not try. For the grand jaunt he settled on an assortment of motorized transport: three Sno-Cats, two Weasels, and a Muskeg. And though they sound like the members of a menagerie, all three are tracked motor vehicles specially designed for cold-weather, oversnow service. They pulled a combined load of twenty tons, much of it fuel, loaded on heavy cargo sleds. For reconnoitering ahead of the main party, Fuchs included two dog teams. This was not a concession to his own sympathies but a simple means of preserving his valuable vehicles from risk.

At the other end of the line, Hillary set out in three highly unspecialized vehicles: ordinary farm tractors which, except for winterizing, were very little changed from the machines which tilled the warm New Zealand countryside. That they were used was the result of economic necessity; that they made it was a happy miracle. He also had one Weasel, which did not make it, and dog teams for reconnaissance.

Fuchs' plan required an intermediate base on top of the ice cap, 250 miles inland and 4000 feet up from Shackleton Station. At this place, called South Ice, was stored fuel which the transcontinental party would take on after the climb from the coast. Between the two was a region where the ice cascaded roughly to the sea, and here the hardest going was expected. As the depot was established by air, it was not until the eve of the final departure that Fuchs discovered just how hard it would be.

With four vehicles he set out on a preliminary shake-down in late October, 1957. He expected to return by air in two weeks with a good road marked out for the rest of the party. On the third day crevasses were encountered, crevasses so numerous, so varied, so treacherously bridged with snow it appeared doubtful that any motorized ex-pedition could get through the country. At times the surface seemed to be a vast shell of snow resting on a few hard ridges of ice. As the machines rumbled across, great sections collapsed and fell, manholes and trap doors opened on every side. It was a fearful scene out of the books of H. Rider Haggard.

On the fourth day the crevasses got worse. The Weasel driven by Fuchs and the sledge it towed sagged partly into a widening hole and stuck. A second Weasel outraced a weakening bridge that collapsed just as the vehicle reached safety, but a few hundred yards farther on it lurched side-ways and wedged into the mouth of an opening just a foot too narrow to swallow it whole. Meanwhile the Sno-Cat suddenly found itself at the edge of the hole which had opened behind the Weasel, and its driver nursed it along the brink and to safety. Not a man of the party was unshaken, with the possible exception of Fuchs, who calmly noted in his journal that, "with three near catas-trophes in 300 yards, we have reached an area from which it will be wise to remove ourselves as carefully and quickly as possible."

But in crevasse country you cannot hurry and be careful at the same time. Fuchs now sent out scouts on skis with long metal rods to probe into the surface to see if it was solid, or, if only a bridge, if it was strong enough to support the vehicles. One day, after two cave-ins and an hours-long struggle to gain a half mile, the party rested on what seemed a safe surface. "Suddenly a rumbling noise like underground thunder surrounded us. Then before our eyes two enormous holes, 30 to 40 feet long and 12 feet wide, appeared on either side of the vehicles. Fortunately, where the prodded route passed between these holes the ice remained firm. . . ." The vehicles crept out and "in spite of this tremendous collapse they were perfectly all right."

Such adventures were harrowing and time consuming. The two weeks estimated for the reconnaissance stretched to five. So intricate was the route through the crevasse belt, the vehicles traveled 425 miles to cover the 250. The delay placed the whole enterprise in jeopardy, for at the other end of the 2,100-mile journey it would be faced with the advancing antarctic winter—a time when theoretically no trail party could survive. But Dr. Fuchs was convinced that once the plateau was reached he could make up the lost time.

One month was required to bring the main body of the expedition from the coast to South Ice. Despite the additional vibrations of eight machines and the threat they presented to fragile snow bridges, there were no serious breakdowns or losses, though one Sno-Cat broke through and hung precariously on the lip of a sixty-foot crevasse for five hours. On Christmas Day Fuchs left his advance camp and set out across the plateau, "going full bore" toward the pole.

Seventy-five miles ahead of the main party the dog teams scouted the trail, their crews reporting by radio, building snow beacons every five miles to mark the way.

The column of vehicles settled into a gruelling camp-and-move routine. The chief hazard now was *sastrugi*—iron-hard waves of snow from a few inches to several feet high, as effective as a concrete tank barricade in hindering tracked vehicles. An essential piece of equipment was a portable welding outfit that was used many times to mend snapped and broken metal parts. During whiteout, when surface and sky blend into an all-over milkiness, steering was done by looking *backward* along a line of flags planted every five hundred feet by the lead Sno-Cat.

Between 9 and 10 P.M. each day the column halted. The seismic crew immediately began boring a thirty-six-foot hole for its "shot." This usually took two to three hours, as the three-inch-diameter cores had to be removed

Sir Vivian Fuch's Sno-cats on the trail; gear is towed on sleds behind.

Royal New Zealand Navy Photo

for examination by the glaciologist. The actual firing of the explosive charge was delayed until the morning so that thermometers could remain in the boring overnight. Temperatures as low as 52 below zero were found. By the time a hot meal was eaten—generally pemmican and cocoa—and everyone settled in, it was midnight or later. After six hours of sleep, engines were started, and the procession jogged off on another day's run. The men suffered principally from minor frostbite and lack of sleep.

On the other side of the continent Hillary and his tractors were having their bout. The climb to the plateau here was not as bad as the road to South Ice. There were numerous crevasses but they were either narrow or well bridged. Only once did a tractor break through dangerously. But the Weasel failed to measure up to expectations and after repeated breakdowns had to be abandoned. The tractors were not completely enclosed and a long stint behind the wheel at twenty below brought its discomforts. While making repairs to his machine, one man was snatched by a terrific gust of wind and broke a rib against a steel tow bar. He was evacuated by air to Scott base. But generally Hillary's progress was smooth and efficient and ahead of schedule.

His specific mission was to scout the road between Scott Station and Depot 700. At this place, on the ice cap seven hundred miles from Scott and five hundred from the pole, a fuel cache for Fuchs' use had been established by air the previous season. Near here both parties would join up, take on fuel, and march home together. By December 15 he was at Depot 700. By the twentieth he had completed the stocking of the cache and marking flags were set out on six-foot snow cairns half a mile apart and spread out for five miles on either side of the depot. On this date Dr. Fuchs, plagued by the awful road to South Ice, had not even arrived at his advance base. Hillary thus had unexpected time on his hands. As he also had an ample supply of fuel, he decided to go beyond the bare requirements of his misssion. He sent a radio message to Scott Station: "We are heading . . . for the pole, God willing and crevasses permitting!"

Beyond the depot there was a tremendous improvement in the plateau conditions. The party was now crossing a large featureless plain, the surface smooth, the altitude over 9,000 feet, the temperature ten to twenty below, and the tractors throbbing steadily. Daily runs were over forty miles. On January 3rd ". . . we had done sixty miles and were looking rather anxiously for signs ahead. I was in the lead tractor and was about to stop for refuelling when I suddenly noticed a black dot to my left."

It was a red marker flag on the outskirts of the Amundsen-Scott Station at the south pole. They camped for the night in high spirits, and before noon of the next day they rumbled into the American camp in modest triumph. The five hundred miles from Depot 700 to the pole had been driven in 9½ days. In the final stages Hillary had made incredibly good progress, a magnificent journey.

Fuchs could not achieve the same, hampered as he was by a large party, more vehicles, and an inflexible scientific program which he refused to abandon, although in the later stages he curtailed it somewhat. His seismic soundings alone were providing information about the subglacial floor of central Antarctica that would soon bear directly on man's concept of the continent. The day Hillary arrived at the pole, Fuchs still had 357 miles to go. "The last 57 miles have been through a rugged field of high *sastrugi*. The vehicles go up and down four-foot ridges as they wend their way through a maze of weird forms carved by the wind from the snow. Every few yards the heavy sledges crash over precipitous places causing damage to runner, towbar, and vehicles. The present average progress is 20 miles a day of 13 to 15 hours." Fuchs, therefore, was also less favored by the terrain. But he kept plodding. And on January 20th all parties met at the pole.

Here in the comparative luxury of the IGY station Fuchs and his men rested, took showers, and went over plans for the rest of the journey. The scene was real enough, but it bordered on the fantastic. A few years before, had anyone seriously spoken of Cambridge professors driving cars across Antarctica and stopping off at the pole for hot tea and showers, he would have been promptly labeled a crackpot.

Summer was running out, and there was still more than half the journey to go. Those who were concerned that an early winter might catch Fuchs still out on the trail advised him to cache his vehicles, return to civilization, and finish the journey another year. But as with any grand project, Fuchs could see the difficulty, even impossibility, of picking up and starting again should he abandon it now. The antarctic is not the back yard; he might be able to return in a year, he might never return.

No, he could not stop now. His vehicles were running well, his men were in excellent spirits and condition, food and fuel supplies were ample. Forty-eight hours after arriving at the pole he was on his way again. Aside from hospitality and friendliness he took nothing from the Americans; he wished to preserve the British character of the expedition and show that the presence of the American base was not necessary to his plan.

Of course, the risk was still there. Should a breakdown or mishap occur, rescue could be made by airplane. But if the weather deteriorated at the same time and made air operations impossible there was real danger. Fuchs might be caught out on the plateau completely at the mercy of the relentless elements—just as Scott had been forty-six years before.

The dog teams were left behind, as the road had already been scouted by Hillary. The scientific program was abbreviated so that greater daily mileages could be made. The Weasel would be abandoned as soon as its fuel load was consumed. "We have no doubt," Fuchs wrote, "that we shall successfully arrive at Scott base."

The column progressed steadily toward Depot 700. Two Sno-Cats dropped into crevasses and were recovered. The steering gear of one failed and had to be repaired. The weather was generally clear, the surface soft but otherwise the best the Sno-Cats had encountered since leaving Shackleton base. The ailing Sno-Cat broke its steering mechanism a second time, and there were delays for repairs and the anguish over men's hands sticking to cold metal as they worked. Beyond Depot 700 the train encountered severe whiteout conditions. Hillary, now a member of the party, tied a rope around his waist and for thirty miles went ahead on foot, testing the surface with an ice ax while the vehicles crept along behind.

The weeks of February passed and, though normally a month of sudden storms and dropping temperatures, the good weather held. The long descent from the plateau was carefully and thankfully made, and on March 1st the tractor train was forty-five miles from Scott base. The next day it pulled into camp in the midst of jubilation.

An impromptu band played the national anthem, *Dixie,* and *My Bonnie Lies Over the Ocean.* The reason for this assortment of tunes is unknown. Some of the rugged Britishers fought to hold tears back.

The problem that had faced Fuchs—now Sir Vivian Fuchs—was the same as that facing any traveler who must get from point A to point B (and often back again) with enough food and equipment to perform whatever tasks are necessary, and with a reasonable amount to spare as a margin of safety. The harsh environment of the antarctic multiples all the usual difficulties of travel in wild and uninhabited places and adds new ones; the "country-side" provides absolutely nothing to the wayfarer except water, and this must be melted from snow at the expense of fuel.

Man has tried the muscles of his own back and legs— and generally failed. Eskimo techniques and equipment borrowed from the arctic and modified to meet the explorer's needs brought success to certain geniuses in the art of polar travel. These include Roald Amundsen, for example, who is well-known, but also such unheralded men as Quin A. Blackburn, who sledged 1,380 miles on the Byrd Expedition in 1934-35, and Lawrence M. Gould, a distinguished scientific leader during the IGY but a good "dog man" too, who sledged 1,300 miles in seventy-seven days thirty years before.

It was success only of a degree. The sheer work of driving dogs, feeding dogs, disentangling fighting dogs, making and breaking camp occupied most of the available time. Also an individual dog or team is sharply limited in the load it can haul. If a large amount of material is to be moved it means either hundreds of dogs or hundreds of trips. Thus, while pure travel or minor investigations were quite possible with dogs, large-scale scientific work was impractical. The dog was already doomed at the time of Shackleton's dismal experiments with the New Arrol-Johnston Car in 1908.

This machine was fitted with a specially designed air-cooled engine; "water could not be used for cooling as it would certainly freeze." The car was provided with several sets of rear wheels to obtain traction on varying surfaces, and a pair of skis for the front end, should this arrangement be desired. All to no avail. The New Arro-Johnston bogged down hopelessly in soft snow, and no matter what type of wheel was fitted they "simply scooped holes for themselves." It did not seem to occur to Shackleton that he could prevent the car from sinking by widening the tread of its wheels, and finally the "motor" was abandoned as useless.

What was required were reliable engines—and these came gradually—and also specialized running gear to cope with the peculiarities of the antarctic terrain: snow of various consistencies (especially soft), the murderous up-and-down waves of *sastrugi,* ice, and crevasses.

The Snowmobile used by Byrd, which had tracks in the rear and skis in front, was a semi-success; it finally bogged down in deep soft snow. (A successful, improved version is presently widely used in the Canadian north.) The Cletrac and Citroën tractors used by him on his second expedition worked much better and firmly established the fully tracked vehicle in the antarctic. In these machines Byrd's men made the first extended oversnow tractor journeys. Improvements were made in the techniques of "winterizing" engines, but the key to operation was the linked track, which enabled the weight of the vehicle to be uniformly distributed over the surface and eliminated direct contact between the snow and rolling or sliding parts. As we have seen, special, extra-broad tracks have enabled even the heaviest of tractors (thirty-five tons) to take to the snow.

During World War II a vehicle known as the Weasel was developed. Fully tracked, light, fast, it has been a reliable favorite of many expeditions in both the arctic and antarctic. The Penguin, a tracked vehicle produced in the Soviet Union, has been highly successful; it is provided with a roomy, heated cab in which a traveling party may work in reasonable comfort. And the Australians have had some success with the DUKW, an amphibious device which may purr through the water and crawl up on a rocky shore with the greatest of ease. It has been used for unloading ships on unapproachable coasts.

In 1939 the United States Antarctic Service produced the Snow Cruiser, a fantastic departure from the orderly evolution of oversnow vehicles. It was a polar Juggernaut

Australian DUKW vehicles churn through the ice and then crawl up onto the shore.

A.N.A.R.E. Photo by George Lowe

worthy of the imagination of Jules Verne, fifty-five feet long, twenty feet wide, and fifteen feet high, moving on four enormous rubber-tired wheels each ten feet high and individually driven by powerful electric motors. Inside, the Cruiser was fitted out like a land ship, with pilot house, sleeping quarters, galley, engine room for the diesel electric generator, and laboratories. On top perched a light ski plane for aerial sorties.

In operation it would be a roving camp, ranging far and wide, perhaps to the pole. Though it sounded like a dream, the Snow Cruiser was actually built at a cost of $150,000. When it reached the antarctic, it laboriously chugged a few hundred yards through soft snow and then stopped, unable to climb out of the hollows its great wheels persisted in making. It is there yet.

The Sno-Cat used by Sir Vivian Fuchs was a tenth the size of the Snow Cruiser but infinitely more effective. It was originally designed to cross the spongy muskeg of northwestern Canada. It subsequently has proved capable of traveling across a variety of difficult terrain. Its body resembles that of an ordinary truck, but in place of wheels are four "pontoons" around each of which rides a linked track. All tracks are driven from a single engine located in the forward part of the machine. The individual pontoons have a degree of flexibility that enables them to adapt to the irregularities of the surface.

The Sno-Cat might be described as a combination of tractor, truck, and four-legged animal! Nevertheless it crawled, rolled, and walked the 2,100 miles from Shackleton Station to Scott Station without a major mishap or failure.

On the six-hundred-mile road from Little America V to IGY Byrd Station, different terrain and objectives required different vehicles and techniques. Any reasonably

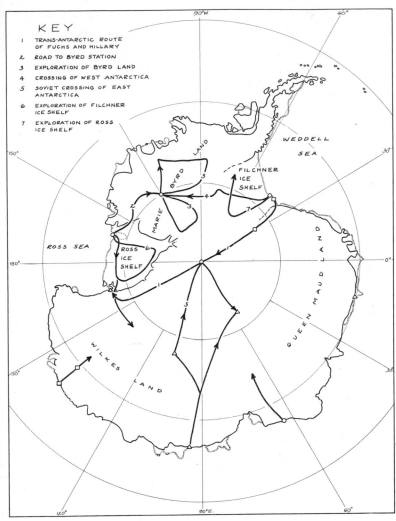

KEY

1 TRANS-ANTARCTIC ROUTE
   OF FUCHS AND HILLARY
2 ROAD TO BYRD STATION
3 EXPLORATION OF BYRD LAND
4 CROSSING OF WEST ANTARCTICA
5 SOVIET CROSSING OF EAST
   ANTARCTICA
6 EXPLORATION OF FILCHNER
   ICE SHELF
7 EXPLORATION OF ROSS
   ICE SHELF

Midcentury traverses in quest of knowledge for IGY.

direct route into Marie Byrd Land must cut across the heavily crevassed belt which marks the line of juncture between the continental ice sheet and the Ross Ice Shelf. The crevasses in this borderland are wide and deep and run in every direction of the compass to form an ice maze which appears to have many entrances and blind alleys but no exits on the far side.

Over this route had to move 380 tons of matériel for the construction of the scientific station. The prime movers were D-8 Caterpillar tractors, weighing thirty-seven tons and capable of drawing a load of over eighty tons. The special fifty-four-inch tracks of these machines distributed the weight so that the load on the snow surface was the equivalent of a man standing on skis. The "cars" of the tractor trains were heavily built sledges which moved on four broad ski runners. Each was fitted with a huge cargo box and outboard racks onto which could be piled additional loose cargo.

The tractor crews slept in wanigans, cosy caboose-like structures which rode on ski runners behind a Sno-Cat, and were fitted out with electric lights and big oil heaters. There was also a mess wanigan hauled by one of the big tractors, in which cooking and eating were done, and which served as a gathering place for the crew. The tractor train was not an entirely new idea, having been modeled after the big "cat swings" which haul cargo on the winter trails of northern Canada.

Leading the train was a Weasel equipped with a "dish-pan" crevasse detector. This device consists of a light framework extending twenty feet or more ahead of the vehicle and fitted with dish-shaped metal electrodes which slide across the snow as the Weasel progresses. An electric signal passes through the snow between the electrodes and is monitored in the cockpit. When there is empty space beneath the surface, indicating a bridged crevasse, the change in the signal sounds a warning buzzer and flashes a red light. With this instrument, which is usually reliable, motoring in crevasse country is immeasurably safer.

When a crevasse is detected, the simplest course is to search along the edge for a snow bridge strong enough to support the traffic. In determining this the snow is probed with long metal rods, or a hole may be punched in the lid and a man lowered to estimate the snow thickness from the amount of light filtering through to the underside. Though the snow bridge may be thirty feet

United States Navy tractor train on the road to Byrd Station. Bulldozer blades are for filling crevasses. Small vehicle at right is a weasel.

Official U.S. Navy Photo

thick and strong enough to support a thirty-five-ton tractor, shadows of men on the surface can be clearly seen from below. The strength of a snow bridge is thus easily estimated by this simple means. Dr. Fuchs, who used lighter vehicles, found snow lids only six feet thick strong enough to support a crossing.

In the event that no safe bridge is found, the tractor train turns back and an attempt is made to find another route through the region. But this can be roundabout and time consuming, and a road may have to be built across the crevasse. This is done by blasting away the snow bridge with explosives, breaking down its edges with bulldozer blades, and filling it in with snow. Such filled-in crevasses will bear heavy traffic, but again in the short antarctic travel season such techniques are costly in time.

There is still much hazard in surface travel through crevasse country. In building the road to Byrd station one life was lost—man and tractor down a crevasse with no chance of recovery. The first tractor to reach the inland plateau was empty. The driver walked many yards behind, operating his machine by means of long lines to the controls—a favorite means among tractor men of avoiding fatal accidents.

For their treks through the interior, Soviet explorers used generally similar techniques, but a new idea was to get away from tractor trains of several units and make each vehicle as far as possible independent and self-contained. "Giant tractors" were built and fitted with insulated duralumin cabins twenty-six feet long and thirteen feet wide.

Inside were a driver's cab, a mess room, a bedroom for eight men, a kitchen with electric stove, a navigator's cubicle, radio apparatus, a snow melter, and a washroom,

all heated by a flow of warm air and all slightly reminis-
cent of the ill-fated Snow Cruiser. Except that the Russian vehicle moved easily on tracks thirty-nine inches
wide, which reduced the surface load to the usual figure
of something less than that produced by a man on skis.
One concession to the train concept was the provision
of a single fuel trailer with a capacity of twenty tons.
This plus the fuel carried in the oversized tanks mounted
on the tractor gave the equipment a range of 2,800 miles,
thus making it unnecessary to depend upon aircraft for
resupply.

There is a twofold significance to the great midcentury
treks. On one hand they have brought a new and valuable
familiarity with the interior of Antarctica. On the other
they have virtually finished the dog team and sledge,
which may come as a disappointment to romancers. But
it cannot be helped. Antarctica has her problems and
will not wait for people with romantic but impractical
ideas.

14

Homo Sapiens Antarcticus

THE TITLE OF THIS chapter is the Latin name a zoologist might apply to the race of men living in Antarctica. It is a little nonsensical, but it is not meant to be completely absurd. Translated, it means *man of the antarctic.* Of course, man did not originally inhabit the antarctic, but he is there now and we must presume that he will stay on there more or less permanently. What is he like?

Most of the distinguishing characteristics of our hypothetical race of antarctic men will be superficial—clothing and equipment, habits and houses—all of which can easily be cast aside to reveal the familiar figure of more temperate regions. But during a long residence in a cold climate actual body changes take place. Acclimatization, it is called, and we cannot discount its long-term effect.

The body has its own heat-producing mechanism which maintains the temperature required for efficient functioning of the life processes—about 100° Fahrenheit. And there is a degree of self-regulation so that without external help the organism can function at temperatures above and below this. Nevertheless the range is rather narrow, and unclothed man is—or was—a prisoner of the tropics.

What was needed for roaming, and especially into the polar regions, was a good suit of clothes to conserve the body's natural heat. But something so seemingly simple has escaped man for most of his history, with the unique exception of the Eskimos, a primitive polar people who long ago happened on a nearly ideal outfit made of caribou skin that enabled them to survive and be comfortable in temperatures of 40° below zero.

The best insulating material for wrapping about the body to keep in the natural heat is a layer of *still* air. But in the antarctic a suit of this material would cause even more serious difficulties than those faced by the famous emperor, and could not be made to remain still in any case. But the still air that is trapped in the fur of an animal pelt or in the interstices between the fibers of man-made fabrics works very well.

Generally the greater the amount of air trapped and the less the amount of material trapping it, the more efficient the insulating process. A good clothing material ideally should be light in weight and of a loose open texture to hold air. Since the air between layers of material is also a reasonably good insulator, many thin layers are in this respect better than one thick one.

But swaddling the body in layer upon layer of insulating material is not the complete answer to the clothing problem, because there are other factors besides mere heat conservation to consider. One of them is wind. A man may be dressed in perfect comfort at a temperature of zero when the air is calm. But if the wind should rise to fifty miles per hour, without any change in temperature, he will immediately be miserable and will soon freeze to death if he cannot get inside or change into better gear. Thus, while the insulating power of still air is high, the cooling power of moving air is equally high, and cold-weather clothing must take this into account—most commonly by covering the insulating layer with a thin layer of windproof material.

Scientists have devised the concept of "wind-chill" to describe the simultaneous effect of both temperature and wind. It may be roughly thought of as the arithmetic product of the "coldness" of the air (the difference in temperature between body and outside air) and the velocity of the wind. A high wind-chill does not necessarily mean low temperature alone or high wind alone. If either of these independent factors is of moderate value the resulting wind-chill may still be high. If both factors are large, the wind-chill will then be very high, and man must provide himself with maximum protection.

The most perplexing factor in cold-climate clothing is moisture—the moisture that is produced by the human body and is constantly exuded as vapor by the sweat glands of the skin. Amounts vary with conditions of physical activity and from one individual to another, but the daily production of water from the skin may be as high as two quarts.

In warm climates the vapor passes unnoticed through the garments to the atmosphere. In cold climates, where the outside air temperature may be as much as a hundred degrees below the freezing point of water, the vapor quickly freezes to ice (hoar frost). If this occurs on the outer surface of the garment, all is well. But if low temperatures have penetrated partway, as necessarily must happen, condensation of the vapor takes place within the garments, and this is bad. The clothes first get wet, then freeze, and quickly lose all insulating properties. What to do?

The ideal arrangement would be to have the water vapor condense and freeze where it will do no harm— such as *between* the layers of a garment. But this will not work if the layers are tightly packed and sealed off from the outside air into which the vapor or frost must be dispersed. It works very well, however, if the garments are loose and there is a degree of ventilation between the layers which enables the vapor to be swept out. But if we do this we are at loggerheads with the first principle of clothing, which is to provide still air around the body.

Since you cannot have both, the practical result must be a compromise: insulation and the retention of body heat vs. ventilation and the removal of moisture. Man stands in the middle, protected but not deliciously comfortable. It is a rule of thumb among old polar hands that an all-over warm and cosy feeling is a danger signal. The build-up of warmth means a decrease in ventilation and all its attendant difficulties. It is better always to remain a little chilly, but dry, and therefore in the end be more comfortable!

All these principles are embodied in Eskimo clothing, and it is incredible that they should have been discovered without the help of science—although it doubtless required centuries of evolution. The Eskimo caribou-skin suit is really two suits, an inner one light in weight and worn with the fur next to the skin, and an outer suit of heavier furs worn with the fur outside.

Both suits are in two pieces, shirt and trousers, with a hood on the outer shirt that may be drawn over the head. The outer shirt is loose and baggy to provide the necessary ventilation, which can be controlled by means of a drawstring around the waist. Hands and feet are clothed in exactly the same manner with two layers of caribou skin. Condensation of water occurs between the two leather surfaces of the caribou skins. *Homo sapiens antarcticus* would do well to be as efficiently clothed as the Stone Age Eskimo.

In the past, explorers have considered themselves fortunate to procure well-sewn Eskimo skin clothing. But now it is scarce because of the decline in the number of caribou and in native handcrafts. It is little used today. And even this good stuff has its defects. It is impossible to keep clean; it cannot be washed. It smells (unpleasantly to some) and sheds hair constantly. It deteriorates readily under the action of moisture, sweat, and body oils. In man's vast inventory of materials, something better has been found.

A variety of practical antarctic costumes has been developed, but all invariably provide a thin, windproof outer layer of tightly woven cloth, such as nylon or cotton poplin. The characteristics of a good windproof material are that it be sufficiently fine to stop the wind from penetrating but not so fine as to retard the flow of moisture-laden air from within. The usual windproofs are in two pieces, a loose shirt and voluminous trousers, all provided with drawstrings and buttons for control of ventilation.

Beneath the windproofs will be found the insulating layers which contain the still air. In this matter there seem to be distinct national preferences. Norwegians have settled on knitted wool in the form of thick sweaters called "Icelanders." Americans have often outfitted themselves with woven wool in the form of heavy flannel shirts. Australians have experimented extensively with padded garments filled with waterfowl down, which has extremely good insulating properties, or polyester fiber, which is more readily available.

Clothing the legs are trousers of wool of various thicknesses, and beneath all is grandfather's standby, a two-piece suit of long woolen underwear, except among the British, who extol the benefits of the "string vest." This is a garment resembling a sleeveless undershirt but of such a loose open knit that it resembles a fish net. The purpose is to provide additional air space next to the body and thus further prevent the saturation of insulating layers with moisture.

Fastenings, especially for outer gear, are buttons or tapes, which are reasonably foolproof and easy to repair. Zipper fasteners are also used, since they are fast in operation, but they are not foolproof when clogged with ice, and they are almost impossible to repair under conditions of cold. Being metal, they also provide a conduction path for the escape of body heat. Caribou mittens (the warmest) or wolfskin mittens provide outer protection for the hands. Beneath will be worn knitted woolen mittens or gloves.

Homo Sapiens Antarcticus dressed for an outing. Ropes and crampons indicate that these Australian explorers plan to travel over crevassed glaciers.

A.N.A.R.E. Photo by Tony Hall

Mechanics who must necessarily have their fingers free may wear very thin cotton or silk gloves to work in for a few minutes before plunging back into the fur mittens for a warm-up. Technicians who must adjust delicate instruments may wear fingerless gloves to enable them to work for a few seconds at a time with bare fingers— a dangerous practice if they are touching bare metal, which in any case should be taped to prevent its freezing to the skin.

The feet, which are farthest from the heart and therefore the hardest to keep warm, are a special problem. At temperatures above zero, when melting conditions are liable to be encountered at the snow surface, footgear must be waterproof. But if moisture is sealed out, it is also sealed in, and some means must be provided for getting rid of it, usually by absorption into thick felt inner soles or a pad of senna grass. The felt must be replaced with dry material at the end of each day. Senna grass, first used by the Lapps of northern Scandinavia, has remarkable properties. As it collects moisture it partially oxidizes and yields up a minute amount of heat. If removed from the boot and allowed to freeze, the moisture forms crystals of ice on the surface of the stems. This is easily shaken off, leaving the grass ready for use again.

At temperatures below zero, when the snow surface is "dry," other precautions are necessary. Body moisture is now liable to freeze inside the boot, or cause the boot to freeze as soon as it is removed at night when on the trail. The pioneers talked much of boots that were "the consistency of iron, agony to pull on, almost impossible to walk in. . . ."

The correction lies in wearing oversized boots—two, three, even four sizes larger than normal—and filling the

Surveyors engaged in mapmaking near Mawson Station.
Note boots and silk gloves on man with theodolite. Garments are filled with down for maximum insulation.

A.N.A.R.E. Photo by J. Bechervaise

extra space with loosely woven socks or wrappings, which are frequently changed and replaced with dry material. The material of the boot is undressed leather, which is porous and allows moisture to pass out and freeze on the surface. Or the outer foot covering may be light canvas-and-leather muckluck, which simply protects the stockings.

The antarctic man will be ever conscious of his clothing, never as fashion, but as a practical means of survival. At 50° below zero if he loses his mittens he may well do as the kittens did and sit down to cry. But it is far more serious, for if he is away from a heated camp he may soon die. These important items are therefore fastened to his other garments with cords. He will carefully note changes in his physical activity and adjust his clothing accordingly.

He takes every precaution to avoid overheating, for this would dampen his clothes and destroy their insulating value. At the same time he does not want to overventilate —risking frostbite thereby—or reduce his mental and physical efficiency through excessive chilling. He will be concerned with cleanliness, since cloth impregnated with grease and dirt loses much of its protective quality. He will be particularly careful of his footgear, keeping it dry, frequently changing his socks, renewing absorbent material daily.

Costumes must vary with the season. In the extreme cold encountered at interior locations maximum protection is required. The Soviet scientists of IGY were outfitted with electrically heated suits for outdoor work in midwinter. Yet in summer when the sun is above the horizon many hours of the day, and the incidence of radiant heat is high, it may be possible to work outside stripped to the waist. At this season also dark goggles are a necessary adjunct of dress.

The glare of sunlight on an all-white world is harmful

to unprotected eyes. The sympton is excruciating pain which drives the victim, tears streaming, into a dark corner—if one is available—where relief is long in coming. This is the so-called "snow blindness" which results from overstimulation of the sensitive material on the retina of the eye. It is not actually blindness; the victim simply cannot bear the pain of opening his eyes and looking at the light. Susceptibility is greatest on overcast days when the sun is not visible and multiple reflections of diffuse light beneath the clouds destroy all the shadows which otherwise provide relief from the over-all whiteness.

In cold climates the body itself reacts to provide protection. This is the acclimatization already mentioned. It manifests itself in a number of ways. There is a marked increase in the dryness of the skin (dehydration) brought about by a constriction in the capillaries just below the surface. The evaporation of water from the skin has a cooling effect, one that is highly desirable in the tropics. But in cold climates the body reverses the process and attempts to limit the cooling effect. Unfortunately the dehydration is not complete, and the not inconsiderable quantity of water exuded even at the lowest temperatures is a meddlesome problem, as seen above.

Shivering is a natural protection against the cold. The involuntary muscular spasms actually produce heat in the surface tissues of the body, but the heat produced is quite small, and shivering is at best a temporary defense. If further cooling takes place, shivering will cease, circulation of the blood in the extremities will be reduced, and the available body heat will be conserved for vital organs in the trunk and head. At this stage the limbs are susceptible to freezing and the individual in question is in serious danger.

If tissues become solidly frozen, the cells are destroyed,

and the part in question is permanently lost. Toes and
fingers are most commonly affected this way. If the freezing is not complete, and some cells survive, the part may
be saved. But this will depend on prompt and careful
treatment. The afflicted region must be warmed slowly,
either in a warm room or by means of gentle warm-water
bathing. There should be no vigorous rubbing or massag-
ing, especially in severe cases, as this would cause further
damage to delicate tissues. There must also be treatment
of incipient gangrene, for wherever dead cells are present this dangerous infection invariably arises.

The best treatment of frostbite lies in prevention rather
than cure. The antarctic man will be constantly alert for
telltale white patches on the skin, especially on the faces,
of his companions. A warm hand placed against the spot
will quickly thaw it and prevent further freezing. If the fingers are nipped, he will bring the hand inside the clothing, where it can be thawed against the chest or abdomen.
If one is alone—which is risky anyway in extreme cold—the
telltale sign is a tight feeling of the skin. Polar travelers
have chewed gum so that the constant flexing of the facial
muscles will serve as both preventative and warning of
frostbite.

In extreme cold the circulatory system will be addi-
tionally taxed to keep the body supplied with the nutri-
tional components of the blood which are oxidized in the
cells to produce local heat. Constriction of the blood vessels will cause high blood pressure. The blood will be
abnormally rich in adrenalin, the regulatory chemical
that keeps the entire body machine poised for instant and
abnormal demands. The excess of adrenalin may be related to the sleeplessness of certain individuals and the
"touchiness" of others.

Despite acclimatization, there are certain deleterious

effects related to exposure to extreme cold. At temperatures 50° below zero and lower, the delicate tissues lining the bronchial passages and lungs can be damaged by slight frostbite. Blood may be coughed, in which case the victim must quickly get into a warmer atmosphere, if possible, or be careful to avoid breathing through the mouth. Breathing through the nose or even through a face mask slightly warms the air and acts as a preventative.

Soviet scientists, faced with going outdoors in temperatures of 100° below zero and colder, arranged to breathe through a corrugated rubber tube whose lower end was fastened inside the clothing, thus assuring a supply of air prewarmed by the heat of the body. In these temperatures face masks and goggles were an absolute necessity in preventing frostbite; outdoor excursions were limited to a half hour or less. After prolonged exposure to cold, fillings in teeth often loosen and fall out. When cold air enters the mouth the metal of the filling contracts by a slight amount, but an amount sufficient to break the bond between tooth and filling.

True acclimatization is regarded as a long-lasting adjustment of the body. There is at present some debate about the permanence of the effects described. For example, is resistance to frostbite in some individuals the result of acclimatization, or is it the result of more careful attention to the mere techniques of polar survival? The answer may lie somewhere between the two.

There is ample evidence that the Eskimos as an ethnic group have greater resistance to frostbite than white men in the arctic. Eskimos simply do not get cold as fast or as easily as non-Eskimos. Among men in the antarctic, those who spend much time outdoors have greater frostbite resistance than those with inside jobs. But resistance is greatest among those who have mastered the techniques of dress and survival. What is needed is further experimentation among men who have lived in the antarctic climate for a long period. The appearance recently of a permanent antarctic population will doubtless provide opportunities for doing so.

Are there mental changes accompanying the physical changes that result from a long residence in a cold climate? In the arctic the Eskimos have periods of temporary "madness"; they run amok, shouting, screaming, quite irresponsible and able to do harm to themselves or others. This condition is rare but well authenticated. Among white trappers what is probably the same malady is called "cabin fever." It has made good friends into mortal enemies in the space of a single winter. The general symptoms seem to be a mild but growing irritability and a tendency to anger easily.

In the past this has been related to the supposedly depressing effects of the long winter darkness. This may be a factor. So also may be the confining aspects of small uncomfortable winter quarters from which there can be no escape for long periods when storms are blowing outside, and men are virtual prisoners. But the subtle change in body chemistry, such as the increase in the stimulant adrenalin, is doubtless closely related to the matter.

During his second antarctic expedition (1933-35) Richard Byrd manned an isolated weather station alone rather than risk the consequences of placing two men in isolation in small quarters for most of the winter. "In a polar camp," he stated, "little . . . things . . . have the power to drive even disciplined men to the edge of insanity. During my first winter I walked for hours with a man who was on the verge of either murder or suicide over the imaginary persecutions by another man who had been his devoted friend."

During the expedition of the U.S. Antarctic Service, one man, depressed and despondent from unknown causes, walked out into the storm intending not to return. The cold air soon cleared his thinking, but by then he was lost, and only pure luck saved him from certain death by freezing. On the other hand, the two Englishmen Lester and Bagshaw, on an expedition to Palmer-Graham Land, lived together in a small hut for a year in perfect harmony—or so they said!

Real or imagined? It matters little, for the results must be reckoned with. Expedition leaders make provision for relieving the tension that is certain to build up during the winter. Books, educational materials, games and amusements, even hobby kits, have been lugged south to head off trouble. The leader also tries to pick his men carefully, not only for technical skill but for mental stability and health. If a man brings worries or problems to the antarctic they are certain to get worse. A varied diet helps greatly, for men quickly grow irritable if their food is monotonous or unpalatable.

In this respect the modern specimen of our hypothetical *Homo sapiens antarcticus* fares better than any of his predecessors. The pioneers constantly sought an "ideal polar ration," a food that would not only be rich in the energy-producing nutrients but one that was not bulky and was simple to prepare under adverse conditions. It must also be satisfying, palatable, and digestible, able to pass through the tropics on a slow-moving vessel without perishing.

Such an ideal does not exist, although it is closely approached in the food known as pemmican, a mixture derived originally from the Plains Indians, consisting of about half dried pulverized meat and half fat. This potent food is quite capable of sustaining man in good health

for long periods with nothing else except water. Supple-
mented by hard biscuit, butter, chocolate, and sugar, pemmican formed the basic field ration of many of the early
expeditions. It survives today as an emergency ration and
as trail food for sledging parties, where dogs and sledges
are still used.

The trouble with pemmican is its taste. Most people,
though not all, have declared it unpalatable, and modern
antarctic man has swept it off his board. With powerful
transport at his command, there is no need to take advantage of pemmican's compactness, imperishability, or
simplicity. Of course, expedition larders have always been
stocked more or less with supplies of "civilized" food for
use in base camps where there are reasonable facilities
for cooking and storage. Amundsen, Scott, and Shackleton
took preserved delicacies and fancy foods for winter use
—but on the trail it was pemmican. Byrd achieved a *coup*
in landing on the ice with 150,000 fresh eggs and 600
pounds of turkey—but on the trail his men ate pemmican.

Imagine, then, if these grizzled pioneers could peer
into the mess wanigan of a modern tractor train crawling
across the frozen plateau on Marie Byrd Land. Here, in
the shirtsleeve warmth provided by an oil stove, under
the light provided by the tractor's powerful generators,
a trail cook painstakingly applies frosting to a batch of
cupcakes!

It is not an exaggeration—beautiful cupcakes on the
antarctic trail, and more besides—beefsteaks if you want,
or French-fried potatoes. The antarctic diet differs little
from the diet at home, and the bigger the enterprise the
smaller the difference. Improved packaging, particularly
the deep-freezing process, and refrigerated ships to carry
the frozen food through the warm regions, have made it
possible.

At the IGY south pole station the crisis in cooking was not that the cook's hands were too cold to hold the pemmican pot, or that the wild flapping of the tent in a hurricane wind had knocked it over and spilled an eagerly awaited meal on the snow, or that a shortage of cooker fuel made it necessary to eat food warm rather than hot. It was none of these things, which had been problems and even minor catastrophes to the pioneers. The new crisis at the south pole was that the layer cakes were not rising properly. (The cause was the overlooked factor of high altitude; a successful recipe was radioed from the flour manufacturer in the United States.)

A corollary to this unexpected state of affairs has been a revolution in shelter, the third fundamental in man's antarctic existence. A modern antarctic dwelling no more resembles those of older times than a frosted cupcake resembles a frozen block of pemmican. It is significant that the pioneers rarely used the word house. Hut was their word, and it seemed better fitted to the drafty cramped quarters they were forced to occupy. Some of the famous early huts still stand, nearly perfectly preserved by the dry cold: Shackleton's at Cape Roydes, Scott's at Hut Point; both now considered historical shrines. A visit to either brings a stunning realization of the primitive conditions under which the heroes lived.

The standard modern U.S. antarctic building is constructed of prefabricated panels four feet wide and eight feet long, each a multilayered sandwich with insulating material in the middle, plywood on either side, and a thin sheet of aluminum on the side which forms the inside wall. Some are fitted with refrigerator-style doors, some with small plastic windows. They are joined edge to edge by a hammered-in spline, which makes a simple, strong, airtight seal. Complete interchangeability of panels

permits buildings of any size with any arrangement of
doors and windows.

Erecting such a building is a quick process, although
it is a little more difficult than block building on the
kindergarten floor, which it slightly resembles. The great
advantage of prefabrication is that it eliminates most of
the carpenter work so tedious and difficult in the cold.

If the building is to be placed on a snow surface, it
rests on broad timber footings which prevent it from
sinking. The floor is elevated a few inches above the
footings, so that interior heat will not melt the snow and
cause settling. Extending outward from the sides of the
building is a verandah of light timber framing covered
with chicken wire and burlap. As the snow accumulates
and drifts, the building becomes completely covered, except for the roof, which is swept clean by the wind.

The verandah is transformed into a tunnel convenient
for outdoor storage. Tunnels to other buildings are constructed in the same way, from chicken wire and burlap,
and after the first season nothing protrudes above the
snow surface except the necessary observation domes, radar
towers, and exhaust pipes. Exit and entry is made through
hatchways in the roofs.

The interiors are heated by oil stoves and forced circulation of air. The lighting system, which extends into the
tunnels and converts them into glowing grottos, is supplied by diesel generators. These also supply electrical
power for diverse other equipment such as washing machines, scientific instruments, and moving-picture pro-
jectors. Water for all purposes is made in oil-fired snow
melters and distributed by gravity or pumps. The buildings are all basically alike, but the interiors are fitted out
for various purposes: scientific work, eating and cooking,
sleeping, vehicle repair, communications, recreation.

Not all antarctic buildings follow exactly this pattern. Each country has produced its favorite ideas. The French, who have been plagued by disastrous fires, favor all-metal construction. The Australians have small, easily erected "box car" buildings. The Russians include carpets and dial telephones in their interior appointments.

On the trail, too, developments have kept apace. The tent has nearly passed into limbo, supplanted as we have seen by the tractorized, electrified wanigan. In semi-permanent locations we find the Jamesway hut, a snug structure consisting of semicircular wood frames covered with thick insulating material—a cold-weather version of the familiar Quonset. But regardless of source or application, the principles are generally the same: prefabrication, high insulating qualities, increased space and comfort.

Homo sapiens antarcticus is thus powerfully arrayed. It is significant that he does not complain of the cold—at least not seriously. The pioneers were always cold. Improved clothing, food, and shelter account for most of the difference, and also improved techniques for their use. The sheer effort of existence is becoming smaller and smaller. Antarctic man now has time and energy left over to follow useful pursuits. The veteran of many seasons, he talks now of permanent occupation or settlement in the Antarctic. But before this can be fully realized the problem of the ownership of Antarctica must be settled. And this is still very much in a muddle.

15

Who Owns Antarctica and Why Do They Want It?

EVEN A MILDLY perspicacious boy is likely to answer the first part of this question with, "Finders keepers." He would be showing insight beyond his years. This ancient rule is actually a principle in international law and has been used by powerful nations in dealing with the ownership of some of the geographical prizes that have turned up in the past five hundred years—including Antarctica. Stated more sedately, original discovery is an essential element in a claim of ownership.

Unfortunately, international law is not so much a set of rules written down by those who are concerned with right and wrong as it is a record of what nations have got away with in dealing with each other.

The problem of antarctic ownership has for the present been settled in a rough way by a process that very much resembles the sharing out of a Christmas pie. The continent, which is roughly circular, has been sliced into a number of wedge-shaped pieces radiating from the center (south pole) and terminating at the coast (which bears a passable resemblance to a pastry crust). New Zealand and Norway have helped themselves to generous slices. Australia has taken two—one of them gigantic and constituting the largest single claim. France, unexpectedly for a nation of gourmets, has appetite for only a thin sliver. One piece of the polar pie lies unwanted, and the misshapen slice that includes the Palmer-Graham peninsula is claimed by three: Great Britain, Argentina, and Chile.

In geographical parlance the wedge-shaped slice is called a sector. As a means of dividing up unclaimed lands it is something new under the sun. Africa, for example, was parceled out in colonial times by quite different means. Interested nations staked and defended claims in the coastal region and let the hinterland take care of itself. Many of these coastal claims survive today, although some have become independent nations in their own right.

But in the polar regions, perhaps because of the pattern formed by the converging lines of longitude, something different was indicated. The sector principle was first used in the arctic by the Soviet Union. In the 1920's this country claimed ownership of all lands *known or unknown* that lay in the wide sector north of its arctic coast. Not only was the sector principle thus introduced to the world, but the Soviets established a second precedent in claiming ownership of lands not yet discovered. The Arctic Ocean was not then fully explored and there was some small possibility of additional land discoveries being made.

The rightness or wrongness of this process cannot be argued. The Soviets have made it stick and were successful in rejecting a Canadian claim to Wrangell Island, which lay within their then newly established "sector." More important, other nations saw something good and copied it. Canada claimed all territory within her northern sector. Other nations looked south and the race for antarctic pie was on. It is interesting that this Russian contribution to world affairs has passed almost unnoticed.

The Russians at present have not transported their sector principle to the antarctic and made claims there. However, it has been announced on a number of occasions that there are good grounds for doing so. The

basis is Bellingshausen's circumnavigation, described previously, during which the Russians claim Antarctica was
"discovered." During the IGY the Russians established
several bases on the continent, and at the close of the
planned program these bases were not evacuated and are
now being manned by Soviet scientists. How long this
will be continued has not been announced. But the name
of the famous Arctic Institute of Leningrad has recently
been changed to Arctic and Antarctic Institute. This gives
a clue to Russian interest, if not ambitions, and it has
caused consternation in Australia, within whose wide
sector the Russian stations lie.

Australia seems to have established its claim on a super-
sector principle. The bulk of Australian antarctic territories lie south of the southern coast of Australia itself.
But to this uncertain process she had added the valid
claim that most of the territory was first explored by
Australian citizens. Thus far the Russians and Australians
have got along in the field most cordially. Australian
visitors to Russian camps have acted as though the Russians were guests on Australian territory, and no one
has denied it.

The same harmonious relations have not been evident
in the contentious Palmer-Graham sector. All three interested parties have energetically sought to convince each
other. The claims of Great Britain, Argentina and Chile
do not actually coincide, but there is much overlapping.
The course of events has been rather involved, but each
nation has doggedly sought to establish the validity of its
own claim. Chile and Argentina are less concerned with
the conflict between themselves than they are with their
joint dispute with Great Britain.

Chilean and Argentinian expeditions have visited various islands and coasts, made formal claims, and raised

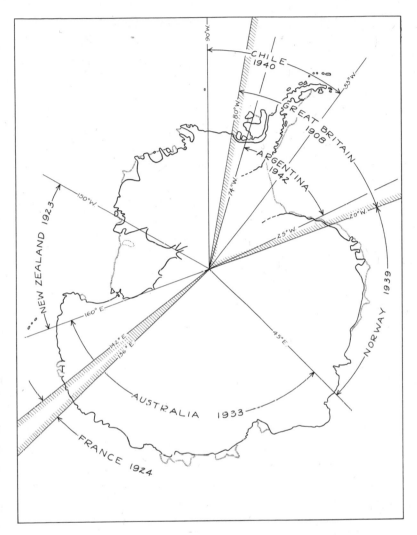

Antarctic pie. Several nations claim territory; their sectors with the date of official claims are shown. British and French claims are shaded for clarity.

flags and markers. British expeditions have followed, removed the markers (politely returning them to their respective countries later), and set up markers of their own.

In 1947-48 Deception Island was the center of a large naval exercise involving most of the ships of the Argentine navy. A British warship was sent south; buildings erected on Deception Island by Chile and Argentina were torn down by the British. In another area Argentines fired shots at a British survey party attempting to land, and drove them off. There was tension in the air, and in the South American capitals will-o-the-wisp rumors of war. Subsequently there were drastic changes in the internal affairs of both countries, and the tension has eased.

The controversy has been heightened by the extent of the Argentine claim, which includes not only a sector of the antarctic continent proper but all adjacent islands. These include South Georgia and the Falkland Islands, which have been effectively occupied by the British for over half a century. The Argentine government has published maps on which these islands are shown as Argentine territory, and a corresponding geography is taught in the schools of that country.

The original discovery of these islands is obscure because records of voyages made in the 16th and 17th Centuries are fragmentary or missing. But it is a further point in international law that effective occupation by settlers and the setting up of administrative control strongly contributes to the validity of a claim of ownership. The establishment of a post office is interpreted as satisfying this requirement. In this regard the British are in a firm position, for every remote survey station has its post office, one member of the party serving simultaneously as postmaster, magistrate, and civil administrator.

Other nations interested in validating antarctic claims have seen the wisdom in this, and most expeditions sailing south have been burdened with mail and postal paraphernalia. Antarctica has thus become a land of improbable post offices. This circumstance has provided the stamp collector with a new field for specialization.

Stamps from the antarctic have been numerous and sometimes beautiful. For example, the Falkland Islands Dependencies, which is the official designation of the British antarctic claim, has issued fifteen stamps, each one bearing an attractive engraving of a famous exploring ship, the whole series presenting a capsule history of this region of the antarctic. But the collector had better not live in Argentina, for this country does not accept letters that have been mailed from British Antarctica!

The United States is in the peculiar position of having two policies about antarctic claims. The first is "official" and has been announced many times during the period beginning with Byrd's first expedition. It states that the United States makes no claim in the antarctic, nor does it recognize the claims made by any other nation. At the present time this policy remains in effect. But beginning in 1939, at the time of the formation of the United States Antarctic Service, now defunct, officials in the State Department, mindful of the increasing activities of more politically ambitious nations, expressed misgivings over the inflexible American policy. It was all quite well to make and recognize no claims, but when the pie was all gone, then what?

This practical line of reasoning caused the U.S. Antarctic Service to be given *secret* instructions to make formal claims in all regions explored. In November, 1939, Leonard M. Berlin, a government surveyor, made the first official United States claim. The area claimed was the territory lying east of the 150° meridian and known as Marie Byrd Land. A message was placed in a bottle and a cairn erected to mark the event.

Subsequent United States expeditions followed a similar practice, and the "American sector" is now well staked out. Beyond this, the United States Government has left the matter in the air. It has never been stated whether these acts constituted an actual claim or whether they were the basis of an official claim yet to be made. The matter was kept secret for many years, and only recently has the present information been revealed.

Should the United States ever decide officially to make known and establish its claim, certain other problems will arise. At its eastern edge the sector lies adjacent to the Chilean claim, or the Argentine claim, or the British

An American party (L. M. Berlin, center) raises the American flag in Marie Byrd Land, 1939. The interpretation of this action has not yet been agreed upon.

National Archives

claim—depending upon which one is valid! Should the United States recognize any one of these claims, the remaining two countries would become alienated. As there is a general desire not to increase the tension in the antarctic, this may be one reason why the United States has not taken a more definite position.

The hypothetical United States claim is lacking in other respects, too. The coast is virtually inaccessible by sea. Only one ship has ever succeeded in penetrating the heavy offshore ice, although the *Glacier,* most powerful of the U.S. ice breakers, has not had an opportunity of attempting it. The interior of Marie Byrd Land has been reached by way of the Ross Ice Shelf, which lies entirely within the New Zealand claim.

In the past there have been no objections to innocuous trespassing for scientific purposes, but if present nationalistic tendencies continue there is no guarantee that this will always be the case. The recent findings of the IGY that the interior of Marie Byrd Land is mostly ice is a further consideration; it may not be worth claiming!

This is perhaps an exaggeration, for the mountain regions of Marie Byrd Land have not been completely assayed and there may be mineral wealth present. It is decidedly untrue of the continent as a whole. If the layman is still skeptical, the specialist is convinced.

Antarctica has important strategic value. We do not ordinarily think of the waters south of Cape Horn as vital to world affairs, yet what if the Panama Canal were blocked? Drake Passage would then be an important gate to the Pacific from the Atlantic—or vice versa. In time of war a neutral Antarctica would cause no harm, but in enemy hands it would provide an excellent base for operations in the western hemisphere.

During World War II the Germans captured much of

the Norwegian whaling fleet and from unknown bases made raids on commerce in the Pacific. Now that large aircraft have successfully operated on ice airstrips, the scope of possible war operations in the antarctic is much larger. The cold climate, the expanses of unpopulated waste, the remoteness from the centers of civilization present special operational problems—but Antarctica cannot be ruled out of consideration in planning for another major conflict.

For fifty years explorers have been preaching the importance of antarctic weather to the world weather pattern. It is still important, and we have reached a point where much of the story is understood, although, as stated

American servicemen at a dedication ceremony at Mc-Murdo Sound. British flags fly because the territory is claimed by New Zealand.

Official U.S. Navy Photo

before, continuous observations from permanent bases are needed. Beyond this, the IGY demonstrated that the whole continent is a vast scientific laboratory in which we may discover facts of utmost significance. (As a matter of fact, we have already discovered some.) While the exact course of the investigations may be somewhat academic, there is practical application to many fields of human activity: world shipping, air travel, agriculture, radio communications, navigation—even space travel.

Economically Antarctica is not yet a strong factor in man's affairs. There has been an antarctic whaling industry for many years and it has made a valuable contribution to world food supplies. The whales are as much a part of Antarctica as the salmon are of Alaska, and we are all familiar with that story. But Antarctica may not yet be viewed as a 20th-Century Alaska. Alaska was near to world population centers, Antarctica is remote. Alaska has mineral resources that have been successfully exploited. Antarctica has minerals, but the uncertainty of their abundance and the difficulties and expense of any antarctic operation have effectively discouraged all interested parties.

Coal has been discovered in Antarctica, but it is not worth going after. The discovery of a vast oil field might perk up interest, because the world desperately wants oil. But it has not been discovered, and oil might be too expensive to bring out anyway. Traces of other minerals have been discovered—gold, iron, tin, chromium, cobalt, copper, lead, nickel, silver, sulphur, and titanium. But a ship voyaging to the antarctic must fill half its cargo space with fuel, and this is hardly practical in a vague quest for "traces." But nuclear-powered ships can drastically alter this picture, and Antarctica must always be kept in mind, especially for metals that are becoming scarce in the regions of the earth's crust more accessible to exploitation.

Some interesting suggestions have been put forth concerning the future utilization of Antarctica's peculiar resources. Everyone thinks of melting the ice cap with nuclear power; this is still in the realm of fiction and not receiving serious consideration yet. Closely related is the suggestion that the barrens of Antarctica might serve as a dumping ground for the dangerous radioactive waste materials from nuclear power stations. If this proves practical it will be regrettable, for one is surely repelled by the thought of turning a continent remarkable for its whiteness and the purity of its atmosphere and snow into a lethal garbage heap.

It has been suggested that Antarctica be used for the storage of food. This is a happier thought. The low temperatures and the dryness of the atmosphere are known to be capable of preserving perishable foods for at least forty years. Food surpluses of "bumper" years could be kept in the antarctic until needed, with no risk of spoilage. Of course transportation to and from may be prohibitively expensive, and this must be considered. Also the present world food shortage may make it necessary to postpone this plan for some time.

High above the earth, at the limits of its atmosphere, geophysicists have discovered a belt of radiation that may have harmful effects on human space travelers (that day is coming; it is only a question of how soon) passing through it. Luckily there are gaps in this radiation wall, high over the northern lights' and southern lights' glow. Should the radiation prove too dangerous for man, these gaps may prove useful. Antarctica could then provide rocket-launching sites—assuming that there were some reason for not launching from the more accessible arctic.

Admiral George Dufek, who led the Deepfreeze operations, was so impressed with antarctic scenery, especially
in the coastal regions, he envisions it as a tourist attraction.
This may be the most practical plan of any. Sailing along
the edge of the Ross Ice Shelf, cruising among the islands
off the coast of Palmer-Graham Land, mountain climbing
on South Georgia—these would be rare and exotic experiences. If such a trip were planned, many people would
sign up for it tomorrow.

It is apparent that Antarctica does not have a super-
abundance of practical plans for the future; it is easy to
get into the realm of conjecture or plain fancy. But there
is sufficient *promise* of wealth and of strategic and scientific importance that vigorous, forward-looking nations
are desirous of establishing themselves in the antarctic—
now, effectively, permanently. The problem of ownership
remains unresolved—and actually becomes worse as interest spreads and more nations look south. The Soviet
Union, especially, is viewed by the western world as a
serious threat to any solution of the problem along the
lines now established. The Russians have no "sector."
They also appear to have little intention of leaving.

One of the brightest events in this dim history was the
promulgation in 1959 of an antarctic treaty among the
twelve most interested nations: Argentina, Australia, Belgium, Chile, France, Japan, New Zealand, Norway, the
Union of South Africa, the Soviet Union, and the United
States. Generally speaking, the provisions of the treaty
establish Antarctica as a scientific preserve. Unlimited
travel and scientific investigation will be permitted any
nation in any region of the continent. There is to be no
political or military activity within the antarctic regions,
and the testing or dumping of radioactive materials is
prohibited. During the time the treaty is in force—a

Rear Admiral George Dufek, commander of Operation Deepfreeze, 1956.

Official U.S. Navy Photo

minimum period of thirty years—no nation may make a territorial claim in Antarctica, but *existing claims will remain undisturbed.*

This provision may be the treaty's greatest strength. During the thirty-year "freeze" of claims world views and national ambitions will change; the desire for territorial expansion may have diminished or disappeared. (There is evidence that the present world is a friendlier place than it was thirty years ago—despite wars!) This particular antarctic problem may be solved simply by withering away. On the other hand, the thirty-year freeze may be a weakness, a vexing procrastination of the world's last great territorial controversy.

To some the ideal solution would be early international control. All claiming nations would relinquish their claims completely and Antarctica would come under the trusteeship of an international body such as the United Nations. Then mankind as a whole, rather than special national interests, would reap its uncertain benefits. This idea is not yet popular among claiming nations, who feel they have much to lose and little to gain. Yet the signing of the new treaty by these very nations is evidence to the contrary. Time will tell.

16

Antarctica and You

WE HAVE COME NOW to the last chapter in a book that has described in a brief way some of the problems of Antarctica and how they were solved, some of the new problems that have cropped up and are now in process of being solved, and some few problems for which solutions are not yet in sight. If we seem not to have got very far ahead but only "in deeper," there is no cause for fretting. It is the way of progress. The end of a book is rarely the end of a subject—particularly a dynamic, changing subject like the antarctic world.

We have seen the possibilities for Antarctica; what of the possibilities for the individual? We cannot buy tickets to the antarctic (at least not until Admiral Dufek's scheme comes into being), and if we are determined to go, other means will have to be devised. Explorers in the old sense of the word are finished. Admiral Byrd was probably the last who could lay claim to that title. But explorers in science and technology have only recently arrived in large numbers. Antarctica is cold grist for their mills, a pantechnicon of problems, which must certainly be years in solving, if indeed there ever can be envisioned a real end to man's expanding knowledge.

An understanding of science—a formal training in science—is the real ticket to Antarctica. Almost any science will do, but more particularly the "earth science" of geophysics and all its multitudinous branches and departments, which deal with the stuff of Antartica, her ice and water, rocks and air.

Make no mistake, the path of science is not an easy one. It involves such matters as mathematics and hard study. But the rewards are many and great, none being greater perhaps than *knowing* while others must wonder, or guess, or (worst of all) simply not care. In the meantime, if your fancy points that way, Antarctica is always there, to read about, to learn about, to aim at.

INDEX

acclimatization, 182, 193
Adelie Land, 30, 104
Adelie penguin, 102, 103
Adventure, 12
Aerial photography, 118, 121
aircraft, use of, in antarctic, 85-86, 116, 124-126, 129
Albatross triphibian, 131
Amundsen, Roald, 64 ff, 120
  expedition to pole of, 65-7
  use of dogs by, 66
Amundsen-Scott IGY Station, 137
  airlift to, 141
  temperature at, 152
  (*see also* south pole)
Andes, 20
Antarctic, 74
antarctic circle, 13, 50
  claims, 200 ff (*see also* name of country making claim)
  continent, Greek theory of, 12
  convergence, 25, 92
  fauna, 23 (*see also* names of animals)
  horst, 21, 120
  ice cap, 16-20 (*see also* ice, glaciers, glaciology)
  treaty, 213
Antarctica
  as a career, 214-215
  as source of cold air, 30
  climate of, 26-30
  discovery of, 36, 40
  first crossing of, 144 ff (*see also* first crossing)
  first landing on, 42

ice of, 16-20 (*see also* ice, ice cap, glacier)
mountains of, 20-21
subglacial nature of, 155-157
value of, 208-211
Argentina, claim of, 201. 202-204
Aurora, 74
aurora australis, 33
Australia, claim of, 202

balcen, 91
balloon ascent, 115
Bay of Whales, 73, 116, 117
Beardmore Glacier, 73, 139
Bellingshausen, Thaddeus von, 37-40, 202
Berlin, Leonard M., 205
Blackburn, Quin A., 173
Bond, Charles A., 126
Bowers, Henry R., 63, 108
Bransfield, Edward, 40
Byrd, Richard E., 16, 26, 130, 132
  discoveries of, 121, 123, 126
  first antarctic expedition of, 117
  flight to north pole by, 117
  flight to south pole by, 118, 120
  second antarctic expedition of, 123
  U.S. Antarctic Service and, 123
Byrd IGY Station, 136
  journey to, 176-178

cabin fever, 194
Cape Crozier, 107

218

Cape Roydes, 73
catcher, whale, 93 (see also whales, whaling)
Caterpillar tractor, 178
Cecelia, 42
Charcot IGY Station, 155
Cherry-Garrard, Apsley, 108
Chile, claim of, 201, 202-204
Christiansen, Lars, 85-86
Citroën tractor, 174
climate of Antarctica, 26-30
clothing, cold weather:
  characteristics of, 183
  Eskimo fur, 184
  for extreme low temperature, 193
  moisture problem of, 184
  principles of, 184-185
  types of, 186-190
coal, 162
continental drift, theory of, 162-163
Cook, James, 11-14
crevasse detector, 178
crevasses, 21, 166-167
  means of crossing, 180
  snow bridges over, 179
Cruzen, Richard H., 124
Curtis Condor aircraft, 123

David, T. E. Edgeworth, 58
Davis, John, 42
Deception Island, 35, 204
Deepfreeze, Operation, 130-142
Deutschland, 74
dogs, use of, 60, 66-67
Dufek, George, 126, 130, 138
DUKW amphibious vehicle, 175
D'Urville, Dumont, 48

East Antarctica, 20
Edisto, 131
Elephant Island, 76, 82
Ellsworth, Lincoln, 129

Ellsworth IGY Station, 155
Emperor penguin, 102 ff
  annual cycle of, 105
  chicks, hatching of, 111
  eggs of, 107, 108, 109-110
  expedition to study, 104-105, 107-108
  mating of, 107
  rookery of, 105
  wintering in Antarctica of, 104, 110
Endurance, 74-75
Erebus, Mount, 52, 58
Eskimos, 182, 185, 193, 195
Euphausia superba, 91-92
Evans, Edgar, 63, 67-68

Falkland Islands, 204
Fanning, Edward, 34
Filchner, Wilhelm, 74
firn, 17
first crossing of Antarctica:
  completed, 172
  difficulties encountered, 165-168
  plan of, 164
  scientific program during, 168-169
  vehicles used for, 165
flensers, 98
Ford tri-motor airplane, 118, 120
flight, first, to south pole, 120-121
  from New Zealand to Antarctica, 131, 138, 139
  hazards of, 118-120
  to south pole during IGY, 137, 139
food, 195-196
footwear, cold weather, 188-190
Foyn, Svend, 84
Framheim, 117
frostbite, 192

Fuchs, Vivian, 164 ff
fur seal (*see* seal, sealing)
fur, use of for clothing, 185-186

Gamow, George, 161-162
Gauss, Carl Friedrich, 50
giant tractors, 180-181
Glacier, 131, 132, 135-137
glaciology, 148-151
Gould, Laurence M., 173
Graham Land, 42
Great Britain, claim of, 201, 202-204
Greek theory about antarctic continent, 12
greenhouse effect, 161
Greenland ice cap, 155

hands, protection of, 187-188
harpoon, explosive, 84, 93
Hawkes, William, 138
Heard Island, 28
Helen of Troy, 16
Hero, 34
    log of, 35-36
Hillary, Edmund, 164, 169
Horst, Antarctic, 21, 120
Hoyle, F., 161
human body:
    acclimatization of, 193
    dehydration of, 191
    effects of extreme cold on, 192-193
    excess adrenalin in, 192
    freezing of, 192
    moisture emitted by, 184
    protection of, 187-190
    shivering of, 191
    temperature regulation of, 182
Husvik, 80

icebergs, tabular, 22
ice breaker, 134, 136
ice cap, antarctic, 16-20, 23, 154

age of, 23, 159
    effects of melting of, 157, 159
    elevation of, 155
    measuring thickness of, 148-149
    theories about cause of, 160-163
ice, glacial, 16
ice of Antarctica, 16-20 (*see also* ice, ice cap)
ice shelves, 21
Ice Shelf, Ross, 54-57
icepack, 25, 51
IGY:
    flight to south pole during, 139
    nations involved in, 144
    results of, 151
    scientific programs of, 144-146, 147
    scope of, 143-144
    stations (*see* name of station)
    traverses during, 146
    unloading supplies for, 133, 136
International Geophysical Year, *see* IGY
inversion, 31

James Caird, 76
    voyage of, 77-78
Jamesway hut, 199

Kainan Bay, 132, 134
katabatic winds, 30
Kolp, H. R., 137
krill, 91-92

Larsen, Carl A., 84
lemmers, 98
Little America, 28, 117, 130, 133, 136, 152, 176
Liv Glacier, 120
Loewe, F., 23, 154

Macquarie Island, 114
magnetic pole, south, 49, 57
manhauling, 60
Marie Byrd Land, 136, 178, 207
  thickness of ice in, 155
Marret, Mario, 105
Martin, Lawrence, 36
Mawson, Douglas, 30, 129
Mawson IGY Station, 157
McKinley, Ashley C., 118, 120
McMurdo Sound, 74, 131, 137
mental effects of polar environment, 194
meteorology, 147
mirage, 32-33
  Wilkes a victim of, 48
Mirny IGY Station, 157
Moby Dick, 92
mountains, 20-21

New Zealand, claim of, 200
Norseman bushplane, 124
Norvegia, 85
Norway, claim of, 200
nunatak, 21

oasis, antarctic, 127-129
Oates, L. E. G., 63, 68-69
oleomargarine, 84
Ortelius, A., 12

P2V airplane, 131
Palmer, Nathanial B., 34-39
Palmer Peninsula, 40
PBM sea plane, 124
pemmican, 196
Pendleton, Benjamin, 34
penguin,
  Adelie, 102-103
  Emperor, 101
  Macaroni, 114
  Rockhopper, 114
  Royal, 114
  (*see also* Emperor penguin)

penguin vehicle, 175
penguins:
  characteristics of, 102-103
  evolution of, 103
  fate of, 114
  food of, 104
  method of swimming of, 102
  species of, found in antarctic, 102
  tobogganing of, 112
  (*see also* penguin)
Philippine Sea, 124, 125
Point Geologie, 104
Pole of Relative Inaccessibility, 20, 138, 144, 152
postage stamps, 205
Powell, George, 36
pressure ice, 25

Queen Maud Land, 86
Que Sera Sera, 139
Quest, 83

R4D airplane, 124-126, 131
R5D airplane, 131, 132
Resolution, 12, 13
Riiser-Larsen, Hjalmar, 86, 129
Rivolier, Jean, 101
Ross Ice Shelf, 54-57
Ross, James, 48 ff
  antarctic discoveries of, 51-54
Ross-Weddell Channel, 20, 157
Rymill, John, 129

Scott, Robert F., 59 ff, 73, 115
  death of, 69
  expedition to south pole of, 61-63
  first expedition of, 59
  methods of travel of, 60-61
  return from pole of, 67-69
sea ice, 23
sealing industry, 37, 43-45
sealers (*see* sealing industry)

seals,
  elephant, 45
  fur, 43-44
  leopard, 47
  species of, found in antarctic,
    45
  Weddell, 47
seismic sounding, 148-149
senna grass, 188
Shackleton, Ernest:
  attitude toward exploring of,
    72
  crossing of South Georgia by,
    82
  death of, 83
  first expedition of, 72-73
  plan to cross Antarctica of,
    73-74
  voyage of, in *James Caird*,
    77-78
Shackleton IGY Station, 164-165
shelter, antarctic, 197-199
Shinn, Conrad, 139
Showa IGY Station, 144
Simbra, 93
Siple, Paul, 31, 151
ski-wheels, 132
Smith, William, 34
Sno-cat, 176
snow blindness, 191
Snow Cruiser, 175-176
snowfall, 28, 154
Snowmobile, 174
South Georgia, 14, 34, 204
  first crossing of, 82
  whaling stations on, 85
South Ice, 165
south pole:
  airlift to, 141
  Amundsen-Scott IGY Station
    at, 137
  first flight to, 120-121
  first landing at, 140
  first winter at, 155

IGY flights to, 137
  reached by Amundsen and
    Scott, 63-64
  snowfall at, 154
  temperature at, 152
  thickness of ice at, 155
South Shetland Islands, 34
Sovietskaya IGY station, 144, 152
Stromness, 80
sun, loomed, 33

temperatures, 28, 31
  averages and extremes of, 152
  explanation of, 153
*Terra Australis Nondum Incog-
  nita,* 12
testudo, 110
Theron, 24
tractor trains, 178
transportation by:
  dogs, 60, 66-67, 173
  motor vehicles, 174-176, 178,
    180-181
  ponies, 61
  (*see also* aircraft, ice breaker)
traverses, 146, 164 ff

U. S. Air Force, 132
U. S. Antarctic Service, 123, 205
U. S. antarctic claim, 205
  difficulties involved in, 206-
    207
  policy on, 205
  secret instructions for, 205-206
U.S.S.R., possible claim of, 202
  sector principle of, 201

Vietor, Alexander, 42
volcanoes, 35, 52, 161
Vostok IGY Station, 157

Weasel, 174
Weddell, James, 74
Weddell Sea, 74

Wegener, Alfred, 162
West Antarctica, 20
Wexler, Harry, 161
whale catcher, 84, 93
whale oil, 87, 90, 93
whales:
  baleen, 91-92
  birth of, 88
  breathing of, 88-89
  butchering of, 96-98
  description of, 87
  evolution of, 87
  food of, 91-92
  harpooning of, 94-96
  muscular power of, 90
  oil contained in, 87, 90
  scarcity of, 100
  species of, found in antarctic,
    90

  spouting of, 88
whaling factory ship, 96-98
whaling industry, dangers of, 98
  establishment of, 85
  growth of, 85
  international control of, 100
  size of catch of, 100
whaling stations, 85
whiteout, 31
Wild, Frank, 75, 83
Wilkes, Charles, 48
Wilkins, Hubert, 116
Williams, 40
Wilson, Edward, 63, 108
wind chill, 183-184
winds, 30
Worsley, Frank, 79

Yelcho, 82